O9-AIG-336

GRADE 4

Curriculum Units

Size, Shape, and Symmetry

2-D Geometry and Measurement

UNIT 4

Mollie activity
time

RL
Julio - RL

Polished Spiral Karin Kuhlmann

"Although the creation of fractals is bounded to strict mathematical rules, the results are always very inspiring."– **Karin Kuhlmann**

Investigations
IN NUMBER, DATA, AND SPACE®

GRADE
4

Size, Shape, and Symmetry

2-D Geometry and Measurement

UNIT 4

Many of the designations used by manufacturers and sellers to distinguish their products are claimed as trademarks. Where those designations appear in this book, and Scott Foresman was aware of a trademark claim, the designations have been printed with initial capitals and in cases of multiple usage have also been marked with either ® or ™ where they first appear.

Editorial offices: Glenview, Illinois • Parsippany, New Jersey • New York, New York
Sales offices: Boston, Massachusetts • Duluth, Georgia
Glenview, Illinois • Coppell, Texas • Sacramento, California • Mesa, Arizona

The Investigations curriculum was developed by TERC, Cambridge, MA.

This material is based on work supported by the National Science Foundation ("NSF") under Grant No. ESI-0095450. Any opinions, findings, and conclusions or recommendations expressed in this material are those of the author(s) and do not necessarily reflect the views of the National Science Foundation.

ISBN: 0-328-23756-6

ISBN: 978-0-328-23756-2

7 8 9 10-V003-15 14 13 12 11 10 09 08

CC:N2

T E R C

Co-Principal Investigators

Susan Jo Russell

Karen Economopoulos

Authors

Lucy Wittenberg
Director Grades 3–5

Karen Economopoulos
Director Grades K–2

Virginia Bastable
(SummerMath for Teachers,
Mt. Holyoke College)

Katie Hickey Bloomfield

Keith Cochran

Darrell Earnest

Arusha Hollister

Nancy Horowitz

Erin Leidl

Megan Murray

Young Oh

Beth W. Perry

Susan Jo Russell

Deborah Schifter
(Education
Development Center)

Kathy Sillman

Administrative Staff

Amy Taber
Project Manager

Beth Bergeron

Lorraine Brooks

Emi Fujiwara

Contributing Authors

Denise Baumann

Jennifer DiBrienza

Hollee Freeman

Paula Hooper

Jan Mokros

Stephen Monk
(University of Washington)

Mary Beth O'Connor

Judy Storeygard

Cornelia Tierney

Elizabeth Van Cleef

Carol Wright

Technology

Jim Hammerman

Classroom Field Work

Amy Appell

Rachel E. Davis

Traci Higgins

Julia Thompson

Collaborating Teachers

This group of dedicated teachers carried out extensive field testing in their classrooms, met regularly to discuss issues of teaching and learning mathematics, provided feedback to staff, welcomed staff into their classrooms to document students' work, and contributed both suggestions and written material that has been incorporated into the curriculum.

Bethany Altchek

Linda Amaral

Kimberly Beauregard

Barbara Bernard

Nancy Buell

Rose Christiansen

Chris Colbath-Hess

Lisette Colon

Kim Cook

Frances Cooper

Kathleen Drew

Rebeka Eston Salemi

Thomas Fisher

Michael Flynn

Holly Ghazey

Susan Gillis

Danielle Harrington

Elaine Herzog

Francine Hiller

Kirsten Lee Howard

Liliana Klass

Leslie Kramer

Melissa Lee Andrichak

Kelley Lee Sadowski

Jennifer Levitan

Mary Lou LoVecchio

Kristen McEnaney

Maura McGrail

Kathe Millett

Florence Molyneaux

Amy Monkiewicz

Elizabeth Monopoli

Carol Murray

Robyn Musser

Christine Norrman

Deborah O'Brien

Timothy O'Connor

Anne Marie O'Reilly

Mark Paige

Margaret Riddle

Karen Schweitzer

Elisabeth Seyferth

Susan Smith

Debra Sorvillo

Shoshanah Starr

Janice Szymaszek

Karen Tobin

JoAnn Trauschke

Ana Vaisenstein

Yvonne Watson

Michelle Woods

Mary Wright

Note: Unless otherwise noted, all contributors listed above were staff of the Education Research Collaborative at TERC during their work on the curriculum. Other affiliations during the time of development are listed.

Advisors

Deborah Lowenberg Ball,
University of Michigan

Hyman Bass, Professor of Mathematics and Mathematics Education
University of Michigan

Mary Canner, Principal, Natick Public Schools

Thomas Carpenter, Professor of Curriculum and Instruction,
University of Wisconsin-Madison

Janis Freckmann, Elementary Mathematics Coordinator,
Milwaukee Public Schools

Lynne Godfrey, Mathematics Coach,
Cambridge Public Schools

Ginger Hanlon, Instructional Specialist in Mathematics,
New York City Public Schools

DeAnn Huinker, Director, Center for Mathematics and
Science Education Research, University of Wisconsin-Milwaukee

James Kaput, Professor of Mathematics, University of
Massachusetts-Dartmouth

Kate Kline, Associate Professor, Department of Mathematics
and Statistics, Western Michigan University

Jim Lewis, Professor of Mathematics,
University of Nebraska-Lincoln

William McCallum, Professor of Mathematics,
University of Arizona

Harriet Pollatsek, Professor of Mathematics,
Mount Holyoke College

Debra Shein-Gerson, Elementary Mathematics Specialist,
Weston Public Schools

Gary Shevell, Assistant Principal,
New York City Public Schools

Liz Sweeney, Elementary Math Department,
Boston Public Schools

Lucy West, Consultant, Metamorphosis:
Teaching Learning Communities, Inc.

This revision of the curriculum was built on the work of the many authors who contributed to the first edition (published between 1994 and 1998). We acknowledge the critical contributions of these authors in developing the content and pedagogy of *Investigations*:

Authors

Joan Akers

Michael T. Battista

Douglas H. Clements

Karen Economopoulos

Marlene Kliman

Jan Mokros

Megan Murray

Ricardo Nemirovsky

Andee Rubin

Susan Jo Russell

Cornelia Tierney

Contributing Authors

Mary Berle-Carman

Rebecca B. Corwin

Rebeka Eston

Claryce Evans

Anne Goodrow

Cliff Konold

Chris Mainhart

Sue McMillen

Jerrie Moffet

Tracy Noble

Kim O'Neil

Mark Ogonowski

Julie Sarama

Amy Shulman Weinberg

Margie Singer

Virginia Woolley

Tracey Wright

Contents

UNIT 4

Size, Shape, and Symmetry

Investigations

CURRICULUM

Overview of Program Components

FOR TEACHERS

The **Curriculum Units** are the teaching guides. (See far right.)

Implementing Investigations in Grade 4 offers suggestions for implementing the curriculum. It also contains a comprehensive index.

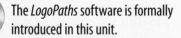

The **Resources Binder** contains all the Resource Masters and Transparencies that support instruction. (Also available on CD) The binder also includes a student software CD.

The *LogoPaths* software is formally introduced in this unit.

FOR STUDENTS

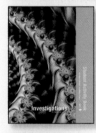

The **Student Activity Book** contains the consumable student pages (Recording Sheets, Homework, Practice, and so on).

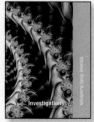

The **Student Math Handbook** contains Math Words and Ideas pages and Games directions.

The *Investigations* Curriculum

Investigations in Number, Data, and Space® is a K–5 mathematics curriculum designed to engage students in making sense of mathematical ideas. Six major goals guided the development of the *Investigations in Number, Data, and Space®* curriculum. The curriculum is designed to:

- Support students to make sense of mathematics and learn that they can be mathematical thinkers

- Focus on computational fluency with whole numbers as a major goal of the elementary grades

- Provide substantive work in important areas of mathematics—rational numbers, geometry, measurement, data, and early algebra—and connections among them

- Emphasize reasoning about mathematical ideas

- Communicate mathematics content and pedagogy to teachers

- Engage the range of learners in understanding mathematics

Underlying these goals are three guiding principles that are touchstones for the *Investigations* team as we approach both students and teachers as agents of their own learning:

1. *Students have mathematical ideas.* Students come to school with ideas about numbers, shapes, measurements, patterns, and data. If given the opportunity to learn in an environment that stresses making sense of mathematics, students build on the ideas they already have and learn about new mathematics they have never encountered. Students learn that they are capable of having mathematical ideas, applying what they know to new situations, and thinking and reasoning about unfamiliar problems.

2. *Teachers are engaged in ongoing learning* about mathematics content, pedagogy, and student learning. The curriculum provides material for professional development, to be used by teachers individually or in groups, that supports teachers' continued learning as they use the curriculum over several years. The *Investigations* curriculum materials are designed as much to be a dialogue with teachers as to be a core of content for students.

3. *Teachers collaborate with the students and curriculum materials* to create the curriculum as enacted in the classroom. The only way for a good curriculum to be used well is for teachers to be active participants in implementing it. Teachers use the curriculum to maintain a clear, focused, and coherent agenda for mathematics teaching. At the same time, they observe and listen carefully to students, try to understand how they are thinking, and make teaching decisions based on these observations.

Investigations is based on experience from research and practice, including field testing that involved documentation of thousands of hours in classrooms, observations of students, input from teachers, and analysis of student work. As a result, the curriculum addresses the learning needs of real students in a wide range of classrooms and communities. The investigations are carefully designed to invite all students into mathematics—girls and boys; members of diverse cultural, ethnic, and language groups; and students with a wide variety of strengths, needs, and interests.

Based on this extensive classroom testing, the curriculum takes seriously the time students need to develop a strong conceptual foundation and skills based on that foundation. Each curriculum unit focuses on an area of content in depth, providing time for students to develop and practice ideas across a variety of activities and contexts that build on each other. Daily guidelines for time spent on class sessions, Classroom Routines (K–3), and Ten-Minute Math (3–5) reflect the commitment to devoting adequate time to mathematics in each school day.

About This Curriculum Unit

This **Curriculum Unit** is one of nine teaching guides in Grade 4. The fourth unit in Grade 4 is *Size, Shape, and Symmetry.*

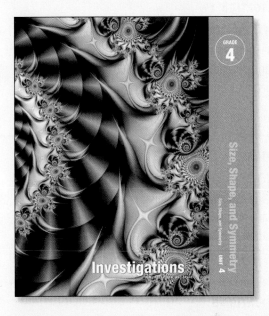

- The **Introduction and Overview** section organizes and presents the instructional materials, provides background information, and highlights important features specific to this unit.

- Each Curriculum Unit contains several **Investigations.** Each Investigation focuses on a set of related mathematical ideas.

- Investigations are divided into one-hour **Sessions,** or lessons.

- Sessions have a combination of these parts: **Activity, Discussion, Math Workshop, Assessment Activity,** and **Session Follow-Up.**

- Each session also has one or more **Ten-Minute Math** activities that are done outside of math time.

- At the back of the book is a collection of **Teacher Notes** and **Dialogue Boxes** that provide professional development related to the unit.

- Also included at the back of the book are the **Student Math Handbook** pages for this unit.

- The **Index** provides a way to look up important words or terms.

Overview

O F   T H I S   U N I T

Investigation	Session	Day	
INVESTIGATION 1 ## Linear Measurement Students estimate and measure length in U.S. standard and metric units, including lengths up to 100 feet. They practice using measurement tools accurately and review perimeter.	1.1 Measurement Benchmarks	1	
	1.2 Measurement Tools	2	
	1.3 Assessment: How Long Is Our Classroom?	3	
	1.4 Measuring Length	4	
	1.5 Measuring Length, *continued*	5	
INVESTIGATION 2 ## Polygons of Many Types Students investigate the attributes of polygons. They focus particularly on quadrilaterals, categorizing them by side length, angle size, and parallel sides.	2.1 Is It a Polygon?	6	
	2.2 Making Polygons	7	
	2.3 Sorting Polygons	8	
	2.4 Sorting Quadrilaterals	9	
	2.5 Assessment: What Is a Quadrilateral?	10	
INVESTIGATION 3 ## Measuring Angles Students identify, construct, and measure angles of varying degrees, by relating them to 90 degrees, the measure of a right angle.	3.1 Making Right Angles	11	
	3.2 More or Less Than 90 Degrees?	12	
	3.3 Assessment: Building Angles	13	
INVESTIGATION 4 ## Finding Area Students measure the area of polygons in both nonsquare and square units of measure, by decomposing shapes and using symmetry. They focus particularly on finding the area of a triangle in square units by relating it to the area of a rectangle.	4.1 Symmetry	14	
	4.2 Symmetry and Area	15	
	4.3 Finding Halves of Crazy Cakes	16	
	4.4 Decomposing Shapes	17	
	4.5 Area of Rectangles	18	
	4.6 Area of Polygons	19	
	4.7 End-of-Unit Assessment	20	

Each *Investigations* session has some combination of these five parts: **Activity, Discussion, Math Workshop, Assessment Activity,** and **Session Follow-Up.** These session parts are indicated in the chart below. Each session also has one or more **Ten-Minute Math** activities that are done outside of math time.

Activity	Discussion	Math Workshop	Assessment Activity	Session Follow-Up
●●	●			●
●●	●			●
●	●	●	●	●
	●	●		●
	●	●		●
●●	●			●
●●●				●
●	●	●		●
●	●	●		●
	●	●	●	●
●●	●			●
●	●	●		●
	●●	●	●	●
●●	●			●
●	●●			●
●●		●		●
●	●	●		●
●	●●	●		●
●	●●			●
			●	●

Ten-Minute Math

Quick Images	Today's Number
	●
	●
	●
	●
	●
●	
●	
●	
●	
●	
	●
	●
	●
●	
●	
●	
●	
	●
	●
	●

Mathematics

Size, Shape, and Symmetry is the first Grade 4 unit in the Geometry and Measurement strand of Investigations. These units develop ideas about the attributes of 2-dimensional (2-D) and 3-dimensional (3-D) shapes, and how these attributes determine their classification. They also develop ideas about linear measurement (which includes perimeter), area, the measurement of angles, and volume.

 LOOKING BACK The work in this unit assumes students have had experience with linear measurement including measuring with a variety of units of length, and finding perimeter. From previous work, students should also be familiar with a range of 2-dimensional geometric shapes, attributes of triangles and quadrilaterals, and with right angles. The work on area in this unit builds upon previous work in finding the area of rectangles and of other shapes that can be decomposed.

This unit focuses on 4 Mathematical Emphases:

1 Linear Measurement **Measuring with standard units**

Math Focus Points

◆ Reviewing the lengths of units of measure (inches, feet, yards, centimeters, meters)

◆ Using U.S. standard and metric units to accurately measure length

◆ Estimating lengths based on common units (centimeter, inch, foot, yard, meter)

◆ Determining when estimates or exact measurements are needed

◆ Finding perimeter using standard units

◆ Recognizing and explaining possible sources of measurement error

◆ Comparing different paths that have the same length

Measuring seems simple enough, but for elementary students it can pose a real challenge. Accurate measurement involves understanding the need for standard units, knowing that you can measure the same length with different units, and using tools correctly. In this unit, students measure with both U.S. standard units (inches, feet and yards) as well as metric units (centimeters and meters). One challenge of measuring longer length is using tools accurately. In this unit, students are challenged to measure the length of their classroom and to map a path that is 100 feet. In both these activities, students work to place their tools in the correct position, leave no gaps between each tool, read the tools correctly, and keep track of their measurements as they work. Students also practice measuring length by finding the perimeter of several objects in their classroom.

Measurement involves being accurate and also being able to estimate. Estimating measurements depends on having a set of reliable benchmarks (e.g., that adults are generally between 5 and 6 feet tall or an inch is about the length of a child's nose). Once students establish a good sense of measurement units, it will be easier to estimate general measurement such as determining that the length of a room is about 12 feet, or a specific window is about $3\frac{1}{2}$ feet wide, or I have walked about one mile.

2 Features of Shape **Describing and classifying 2-dimensional figures**

Math Focus Points

◆ Defining polygons as closed figures with line segments as sides, and vertices

◆ Classifying polygons by attribute, including number of sides, length of sides, and size of angles

◆ Combining polygons to make new polygons

◆ Recognizing number of sides as a descriptor of various polygons

◆ Developing vocabulary to describe attributes and properties of quadrilaterals

◆ Understanding the relationship between squares and rectangles

Geometric shapes can be viewed by various attributes, such as length of sides, size of angles, number of sides, and number of angles. Geometric definitions are based on identifying a set of shapes that have a common attribute. For instance, grouping all polygons that have four sides results in defining the set of quadrilaterals. Within the set of quadrilaterals, further grouping by a different attribute results in more detailed definitions.

In this unit, students work on understanding how looking at different attributes, and not considering others, is how we name geometric shapes. Consider the three examples below. Shapes A, B, and C are all quadrilaterals because the only attribute being focused on is the number of sides. (Angles and length of sides are not considered.) Shapes A and C are rectangles because they are quadrilaterals with four right angles. (Length of sides is not considered.) Shapes B and C are rhombuses because they are quadrilaterals with four sides the same length. (Angles are not considered.) Shape C is a square because it is a quadrilateral, with 4 right angles, and sides that are the same length.

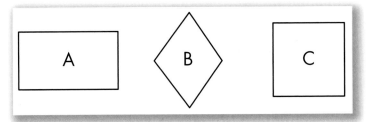

Students focus particularly on quadrilaterals in this unit. They work on expanding their consideration of four-sided figures beyond squares and rectangles, and recognizing that quadrilaterals can have angles of different sizes as well as sides of different lengths.

3 Features of Shape Describing and measuring angles

Students combine polygons to create shapes with right angles.

Math Focus Points

◆ Identifying a right angle as 90 degrees

◆ Measuring acute angles by relating them to 90 degrees

◆ Using known angles to find the measure of other angles

In a polygon, the length of the sides interacts with another attribute, the size of its angles, to form the shape of the object. In this unit, students examine angle size in relation to one kind of angle that they are familiar with from their work in previous grades—a right angle. Students often visualize a right angle as the corner of a rectangle or square. With this as their reference point, they find the measure of other angles, some that are smaller than a right angle, and some that are larger. Angles are measured in terms of degrees or an amount of turning. Because a full turn is 360 degrees, and a right angle is a quarter of a full turn, a right angle is 90 degrees. Students compare other angles to 90 degrees in a concrete way, using the fixed angles of the Power Polygons. For instance, if three of the same angles fit together to form a right angle, then each of the smaller angles must be $\frac{1}{3}$ of 90 degrees, or 30 degrees. Students work on determining the size of angles using this idea, so that they begin to build an understanding of the relative size of both acute (less than 90 degrees) and obtuse (greater than 90 degrees) angles.

4 Area Measurement **Finding and understanding area**

Math Focus Points

◆ Finding the area of symmetrical designs

◆ Understanding that the larger the unit of area, the smaller the number of units needed to measure the area

◆ Dividing irregular polygons into two shapes that have equal area

◆ Finding the area of polygons by decomposing shapes

◆ Finding the area of polygons using square units

◆ Finding the area of rectangles

◆ Finding the area of triangles in relation to the area of rectangles

Area is the amount of space a given figure or polygon covers. In this unit, students deepen their understanding of area by first working with nonregular polygons called "Crazy Cakes." Dividing these "cakes" so that two people get an equal amount helps students understand that area can be *decomposed*—that is, broken into smaller parts—while the area itself is maintained. This is an important understanding as students begin measuring the area of polygons: knowing that they can find the area of smaller shapes within the original polygon, and then combine those parts to find the total area.

Students then find area by determining the number of units that cover a certain shape completely. These units may be other shapes that fit together to cover the shape whose area is being measured. For example, the yellow hexagonal Power Polygon™ is covered by six of the green triangular Power Polygons. So the area of the hexagon is the same as the area of six of the triangles.

The unit of measure for area is square units. Using polygons on the geoboard, students find the area of polygons in square units. While the unit of measure is a square, an important element in finding area with square units is to also consider the area of triangles. Since two right triangles fit together to make a rectangle, a triangle can be seen as half the area of the rectangle. Students use this knowledge to help them find the area of polygons that are composed of rectangles and triangles.

This Unit also focuses on

◆ Making designs with mirror symmetry

Ten-Minute Math activities focus on

- Organizing and analyzing visual images

- Developing language and concepts needed to communicate about spatial relationships

- Decomposing images of 2-D shapes and then recombining them to make a given design

- Generating equivalent expressions for a number using particular constraints

- Practicing computation skills

- Using notation to record expressions

LOOKING FORWARD

Students will continue to use attributes of shape to classify, categorize, and define various geometric shapes as this work on shape is extended in the next grade. The work on angles in this unit will be the basis for student work determining angles measures in the future. The measurement work in this unit will be extended in future grades to include examining area and perimeter of similar shapes and in finding the area of more complex polygons.

Technology Note

Introducing the Software   The *LogoPaths* software is introduced to students in this unit. If you are planning to use the software, you will need to familiarize yourself with it. For information about the *LogoPaths* software, refer to the *Software Support Reference Guide* found on the CD. To prepare to integrate this work into your classroom and to manage the computer environment, see **Teacher Note:** Introducing and Managing *LogoPaths* on page 151, and **Teacher Note:** About Mathematics in the *LogoPaths* Software on page 153, for further support and information.

Assessment

IN THIS UNIT

ONGOING ASSESSMENT: Observing Students at Work

The following sessions provide **Ongoing Assessment: Observing Students at Work** opportunities:

- **Session 1.1, pp. 24 and 26**
- **Session 1.2, pp. 30 and 31**
- **Session 1.3, pp. 38 and 40**
- **Session 1.4, pp. 43–44**
- **Session 2.1, pp. 56 and 59**
- **Session 2.2, p. 63**
- **Session 2.3, pp. 71 and 72–73**

- **Session 2.4, pp. 76 and 77**
- **Session 2.5, p. 82**
- **Session 3.1, p. 91**
- **Session 3.2, pp. 96, 97, and 99**
- **Session 3.3, pp. 105 and 106**
- **Session 4.1, pp. 114 and 115**

- **Session 4.2, pp. 118–119**
- **Session 4.3, pp. 125 and 126**
- **Session 4.4, p. 132**
- **Session 4.5, p. 139**
- **Session 4.6, p. 143**
- **Session 4.7, p. 147**

WRITING OPPORTUNITIES

The following sessions have **writing** opportunities for students to explain their mathematical thinking:

- **Session 1.3, p. 37**
  Student Activity Book, p. 8

- **Session 1.4, pp. 43–44, 46**
  Student Activity Book, pp. 11–13

- **Session 2.4, pp. 75–76**
  Student Activity Book, p. 29

- **Session 3.2, pp. 96–97**
  Student Activity Book, pp. 41–43

- **Session 4.1, p. 115**
  Student Activity Book, p. 52

- **Sessions 4.4 and 4.5, p. 132 and 139**
  Student Activity Book, pp. 63–64

- **Session 4.5, p. 134**
  Student Activity Book, p. 66

- **Session 4.5, p. 138**
  Student Activity Book, pp. 67–68

PORTFOLIO OPPORTUNITIES

The following sessions have work appropriate for a **portfolio:**

- **Session 1.3, pp. 38–39**
  M13, *Assessment: How Long Is Our Classroom?*

- **Session 2.5, p. 82**
  M21, *Assessment: What is a Quadrilateral?*

- **Session 3.2, pp. 96–97**
  Student Activity Book, pp. 41–43

- **Session 4.6, pp. 142–143**
  Student Activity Book, pp. 70–72

- **Session 4.7, pp. 147–148**
  M27–M28, End-of-Unit Assessment

Assessing the Benchmarks

Observing students as they engage in conversation about their ideas is a primary means to assess their mathematical understanding. Consider all of your students' work, not just the written assessments. See the chart below for suggestions about key activities to observe.

 Checklist Available

Benchmarks in This Unit	Key Activities to Observe	Assessment
1. Use appropriate measurement tools to measure distance.	**Sessions 1.3, 1.4 and 1.5:** Perimeter Problems	**Session 1.3:** How Long Is Our Classroom? ✓
2. Identify quadrilaterals as any four-sided closed figure.	**Session 2.4:** Sorting Quadrilaterals	**Session 2.5:** What Is a Quadrilateral? **Session 4.7:** End-of-Unit Assessment, Problem 1
3. Know that a right angle measures 90 degrees, and use this as a landmark to find angles of 30, 45, and 60 degrees.	**Sessions 3.2 and 3.3:** Measuring and Building Angles	**Session 3.3:** Building Angles ✓ **Session 4.7:** End-of-Unit Assessment, Problem 1
4. Find the area of polygons using a square unit of measure.	**Session 4.3:** Crazy Cakes **Session 4.6:** Area of Polygons	**Session 4.7:** End-of-Unit Assessment, Problem 2

Relating the Mathematical Emphases to the Benchmarks

Mathematical Emphases	Bench marks
Linear Measurement Measuring with standard units	1
Features of Shape Describing and classifying 2-dimensional figures	2
Features of Shape Describing and measuring angles	3
Area Measurement Finding and understanding area	4

Ten-Minute Math

I N   T H I S   U N I T

Ten-Minute Math offers practice and review of key concepts for this grade level. These daily activities, to be done in ten minutes outside of math class, are introduced in a unit and repeated throughout the grade. Specific directions for the day's activity are provided in each session. For the full description and variations of each classroom activity, see *Implementing Investigations in Grade 4*.

Activity	Introduced	Full Description of Activity and Its Variations
Quick Images: 2-D	Unit 1, Session 2.1	*Implementing Investigations in Grade 4*
Today's Number: Broken Calculator	Unit 2, Session 1.1	*Implementing Investigations in Grade 4*

Today's Number: Broken Calculator

Students write several different addition and subtraction expressions that equal a given number. They are given constraints, in the context of broken calculator keys that define the operations and the numbers they can use. Students practice and develop flexibility with computation skills.

Math Focus Points

◆ Generating equivalent expressions for a number using particular constraints

◆ Practicing computation skills

◆ Using notation to record expressions

Quick Images: 2-D

Students visualize and analyze images of 2-D geometric figures. After briefly viewing an image of a 2-D design, students draw it from the mental image they formed during the brief viewing.

Math Focus Points

◆ Organizing and analyzing visual images

◆ Developing language and concepts needed to communicate about spatial relationships

◆ Decomposing images of 2-D shapes and then recombining them to make a given design

Practice and Review

Practice and review play a critical role in the *Investigations* program. The following components and features are available to provide regular reinforcement of key mathematical concepts and procedures.

Books	Features	In This Unit . . .
Curriculum Unit	**Ten-Minute Math** offers practice and review of key concepts for this grade level. These daily activities, to be done in ten minutes outside of math class, are introduced in a unit and repeated throughout the grade. Specific directions for the day's activity are provided in each session. For the full description and variations of each classroom activity, see *Implementing Investigations in Grade 4*.	• **All sessions**
Student Activity Book	**Daily Practice** pages in the *Student Activity Book* provide one of three types of written practice: **reinforcement** of the content of the unit, **ongoing review,** or **enrichment** opportunities. Some Daily Practice pages will also have Ongoing Review items with multiple-choice problems similar to those on standardized tests.	• **All sessions**
	Homework pages in the *Student Activity Book* are an extension of the work done in class. At times they help students prepare for upcoming activities.	• **Session 1.1** • **Session 3.3** • **Session 1.2** • **Session 4.1** • **Session 1.3** • **Session 4.3** • **Session 2.3** • **Session 4.4** • **Session 2.5** • **Session 4.6** • **Session 3.2**
Student Math Handbook	**Math Words and Ideas** in the *Student Math Handbook* are pages that summarize key words and ideas. Most Words and Ideas pages have at least one exercise.	• **Student Math Handbook, pp. 54, 101–117**
	Games pages are found in a section of the *Student Math Handbook*.	• **No games are introduced in this unit.**

Supporting the Range of Learners

Sessions	1.1	1.2	1.3	1.4	2.1	2.2	2.3	2.5	3.1	3.2	3.3	4.1	4.2	4.3	4.4	4.6	4.7
Intervention	•	•	•	•	•	•				•	•		•	•	•	•	•
Extension	•	•		•			•	•	•	•	•		•		•		
ELL	•				•	•						•					

Intervention

Suggestions are made to support and engage students who are having difficulty with a particular idea, activity, or problem.

Extension

Suggestions are made to support and engage students who finish early or may be ready for additional challenge.

English Language Learners (ELL)

In this unit, students expand their knowledge of shapes and their attributes. They practice estimating and measuring lengths and perimeters, and learn to find the areas of various 2-dimensional figures. While the use of hands-on activities and visual supports will help students grasp these concepts, English Language Learners may be challenged by the amount of new vocabulary in this unit. You can help by emphasizing key terms in the context of each session's activities. For additional support, you can preview or review some sessions with small groups of English Language Learners, using rulers, yard- and metersticks, Crazy Cakes, Geoboards, and Power Polygons for visual reinforcement. Remind students to refer to the Math Words and Ideas pages on 2-D geometry and measurement in the *Student Math Handbook* for additional vocabulary support.

Some English Language Learners may lack the language necessary to explain their reasoning and to answer process-oriented questions such as What was challenging about this work? or How did you do it? You may need to offer different versions of the questions, such as Was this work easy or hard? or Can you show me how you did this? Student responses will vary depending on their level of English proficiency. Help students who respond orally by rephrasing their responses and modeling the use of geometric and other mathematical vocabulary as you do so.

Finally, you can have students write down their explanations. If they are not ready to do so, you can transcribe their words and then ask them to read the words back to you. Through repeated exposure and practice, English Language Learners will develop the skills and confidence to use this language on their own.

Working with the Range of Learners: Classroom Cases is a set of episodes written by teachers that focuses on meeting the needs of the range of learners in the classroom. In the first section, *Setting up the Mathematical Community,* teachers write about how they create a supportive and productive learning environment in their classrooms. In the next section, *Accommodations for Learning,* teachers focus on specific modifications they make to meet the needs of some of their learners. In the last section, *Language and Representation,* teachers share how they help students use representations and develop language to investigate and express mathematical ideas. The questions at the end of each case provide a starting point for your own reflection or for discussion with colleagues. See *Implementing Investigations in Grade 4* for this set of episodes.

Mathematical Emphasis

Linear Measurement Measuring with standard units

Math Focus Points

◆ Reviewing the lengths of units of measure (inches, feet, yards, centimeters, meters)

◆ Using U.S. standard and metric units to accurately measure length

◆ Estimating lengths based on common units (centimeter, inch, foot, yard, meter)

◆ Determining when estimates or exact measurements are needed

◆ Finding perimeter using standard units

◆ Recognizing and explaining possible sources of measurement error

◆ Comparing different paths that have the same length

Linear Measurement

	Student Activity Book	Student Math Handbook	Professional Development: Read Ahead of Time	
SESSION 1.1 p. 22				
Measurement Benchmarks Students review what linear measurement is and the tools used to measure length. They find objects that equal several measurement units (1 centimeter, 1 inch, 1 foot, 1 yard, 1 meter) and then use these benchmarks to estimate lengths inside and outside their classroom.	1–4	101–102	• **Mathematics in this Unit**, p. 10 • **Teacher Note:** Introducing Benchmarks, p. 150 • **Teacher Note:** Metric and U.S. Standard Measures, p. 149 • **Part 4: Ten-Minute Math** in *Implementing Investigations in Grade 4:* Today's Number	
SESSION 1.2 p. 28				
Measurement Tools Students use measurement tools to measure the lengths they previously estimated with benchmarks. They discuss situations in which estimates of length are sufficient and when exact measures are needed.	2, 4–6	101, 103		
SESSION 1.3 p. 33				
Assessment: How Long Is Our Classroom? Students review how to measure a perimeter and then begin a three-day math workshop in which they practice measuring lengths (including an optional computer activity, *LogoPaths: Missing Measures*).	7–10	103–105	• **Teacher Note:** Introducing and Managing *LogoPaths*, p. 151 • **Teacher Note:** About the Mathematics in the *LogoPaths* Software, p. 153	
SESSION 1.4 p. 41				
Measuring Length Students continue to measure lengths in Math Workshop, now measuring a path that is 100 feet long.	7–8, 11–13	103–105		
SESSION 1.5 p. 47				
Measuring Length, *continued* Students continue to measure lengths in Math Workshop. They compare their paths of 100 feet and discuss how they are all the same length but look different.	7–8, 11, 14	101–105		

Materials to Gather	Materials to Prepare
• **Rulers** (1 per student) • **Yardsticks/metersticks** (1 per group of 3–4)	• **M9–M10, Family Letter** Make copies. (1 per student) • **Chart paper** Label the chart paper "Benchmarks." Create two columns titled "Units" and "Benchmarks." In the units column, list "centimeter," "inch," "foot," "meter," and "yard."
• **Rulers** (1 per student) • **Yardsticks/metersticks** (1 per group of 3–4) • **Scissors** (1 per student)	• **M11–M12, Family Letter** Make copies. (1 per student) • **Chart paper (or board)** See Session 1.2 for list of questions. • **Chart paper** Create two columns, one titled "Exact Measures" and the other "Estimated Measures."
• **Rulers** (1 per student) • **Yardsticks/metersticks** (1 per group of 3–4) • **Blank paper** (1 sheet per pair)	• **M1–M3, *LogoPaths: Missing Measures*** Make copies. (1 per student) • **Chart paper (or board)** See page 35 for figure. • **M8, Assessment Checklist: How Long Is Our Classroom?** Make copies. (1 per 9 students) ☑ • **M13, Assessment: How Long Is Our Classroom?** Make Copies. (1 per student) • **Computers with *LogoPaths* software installed** (optional)
• **M1–M3, *LogoPaths: Missing Measures*** (from Session 1.3) • **M8, Assessment Checklist: How Long Is Our Classroom?** ☑ (from Session 1.3) • **M13, Assessment: How Long Is Our Classroom** (from Session 1.3) • **Rulers** (1 per student); **Yardsticks/metersticks** (1 per group of 3–5); **Masking tape** (as needed)	• **Computers with *LogoPaths* software installed** (optional)
• **Rulers** (1 per student); **Yardsticks/metersticks** (1 per group of 3–5); **Masking tape** (as needed) • **M1–M3, *LogoPaths: Missing Measures*** (from Session 1.3)	• **Computers with *LogoPaths* software installed** (optional)

☑ Checklist Available

Measurement Benchmarks

Math Focus Points

◆ Reviewing the lengths of units of measure (inches, feet, yards, centimeters, meters)

◆ Using U.S. standard and metric units to accurately measure length

◆ Estimating lengths based on common units (centimeter, inch, foot, yard, meter)

Vocabulary

area	foot
volume	yard
perimeter	centimeter
linear	meter
measurement	benchmark
inch	

Today's Plan		Materials
ACTIVITY ❶ **Reviewing Linear Measurements and Measurement Tools**	20 MIN CLASS	• *Student Activity Book,* p. 1 • Rulers; yardsticks/metersticks
ACTIVITY ❷ **Using Measurement Benchmarks and Estimating Length**	30 MIN CLASS PAIRS	• *Student Activity Book,* p. 2 • Chart: "Benchmarks"*
DISCUSSION ❸ **Why Do Our Measurements Differ?**	10 MIN CLASS	
SESSION FOLLOW-UP ❹ **Daily Practice and Homework**		• *Student Activity Book,* pp. 3–4 • M9–M10, Family Letter* • *Student Math Handbook,* p. 101–102

*See *Materials to Prepare,* p. 21.

Ten-Minute Math

Today's Number: Broken Calculator Students create five expressions that equal 1,800. They must use either subtraction or addition in their expressions. The 1 and 8 keys are broken. Have two or three students share their equations and explain how they know that the answer is correct. (Examples: 2,000 − 200 = 1,800 or 900 + 900 = 1,800)

ACTIVITY

Reviewing Linear Measurements and Measurement Tools

20 MIN   CLASS

In this unit, students measure length, angles, and area and study the properties of shapes. They begin with linear measure by first reviewing tools they worked with in Grade 3.

For the next few days, we will be measuring different lengths. For example, we will in a day or two find out how long our classroom is. Let's look around our room. What else about our classroom could we measure?

Allow students some time to consider the question. Students might notice that they could measure the length and width, the space the floor covers (area), the inside space of the whole room (volume), or the perimeter of a wall or the floor. As students describe an aspect of measurement, offer the appropriate math word (e.g., if a student identifies the border of one wall, identify that as the perimeter).

Highlight for students that there are many aspects of objects and space that can be measured, and right now we are going to focus on *linear measurement* (length).

When we measure the length of an object, there are a few different units that we can use. Can you name some of them?

Students should be able to identify inches, feet, yards, centimeters, and meters. The U.S. standard units may be more familiar to them than the metric.

Identify the tools that students will be using: a ruler with inches on one side and centimeters on the other, and metersticks with centimeters on one side and inches on the other (showing one yard and about three inches).❶ Direct student attention to *Student Activity Book* page 1.

We will find objects in the classroom that are equal to each unit of these measurement tools in length. Let's practice. Does anyone see something that may be about one foot long?

Try one or two other examples, perhaps using one centimeter and a yard. The goal of this session is to help students begin to recognize the lengths of these standard units so they can learn to estimate lengths easily and fairly accurately.❷

Teaching Note

❶ **Metersticks and yardsticks** You are provided with eight metersticks/yardsticks for work in this unit. Many classrooms are already equipped with measurement tools and measurement is often a topic in other subjects. If you have separate metersticks and yardsticks, use them for this activity because it may help some students clearly distinguish between meters and yards.

Math Note

❷ **Yards and Meters** Yards and meters are close in length (a meter is about 3 inches longer than a yard). In this activity, students may find objects that are close to the length of a yard and a meter, so the benchmark for both a yard and a meter may be the same. It is useful for students to know that these lengths are similar but that a meterstick is slightly longer.

Name		Date
Size, Shape, and Symmetry		

Measurement Benchmarks

Use a ruler, a yardstick, and a meter stick to find objects that are about as long as these measurement units. Record what you find.

Centimeter	Inch	Foot
Example: the tip of my pencil		

Yard	Meter
	Example: the height of the wall from the floor to the board

Session 1.1   Unit 4 1

▲ **Student Activity Book, p. 1**

Professional Development

❸ **Teacher Note:** Introducing Benchmarks, p. 150

ONGOING ASSESSMENT: Observing Students at Work

Students review the length of common linear measurement tools, by finding benchmarks for each unit.

- **Are students trying out objects appropriately?** If they are looking for lengths equal to a yard, do they try objects that are close to that?

DIFFERENTIATION: Supporting the Range of Learners

Intervention If students are unfamiliar with any of these tools, this is a good opportunity for them to become familiar with the tool and its length.

Extension If students are already comfortable with identifying these measurements, challenge them to find other lengths, such as three feet or six centimeters.

ACTIVITY

30 MIN   CLASS   PAIRS

2 Using Measurement Benchmarks and Estimating Length

Use students' work on the previous activity to introduce the use of the term *benchmarks* for various units of measure.❸

Refer students to the chart labeled "Benchmarks" that you prepared for this session.

You just used several tools to find things that are about the same size as a particular unit. For example, you found that my computer is about one foot wide, your fingernail is about one centimeter wide, and our desks are about one yard off the floor. Let's list more of these benchmarks on our chart. Then we can have lots of useful benchmarks to choose from as we work on measuring.

Collect a few examples for each unit of measurement. Let students know that they can add to the list throughout the unit.

Let's talk about how you could use some of these things to help you estimate lengths. Suppose you had a spool of ribbon and you needed to cut a ribbon about two feet long, but you didn't have any measurement tools. Is there something you could use instead?

As students suggest ideas for ways to estimate the length of something in feet, remind them to consider the objects they just found. For example, since they know the long side of their notebook is about one foot, they could line up a notebook along the edge to find about two feet.

The things we can use to help us estimate length are called benchmarks. A benchmark is something familiar that is the same size—or almost the same size—as a unit of measure. Benchmarks can help you get a sense of, and remember, how long these units are.

Some benchmarks that students suggest will work for everyone in the class; for example, a sheet of notebook paper is about one foot long. Students may also suggest "personal" benchmarks that will not work for everyone. For example, your nose may be about one inch long, or the length from your elbow to your wrist may be about one foot. But these may not be accurate for everyone.

The reason we want to find some benchmarks for each unit is so that we can all get a sense of how big these units are without having to always rely on a tool. If I walk into this classroom, I want to be able to make a good estimate as to how long it is. If I need a piece of wood that is three feet long, it is useful to be able to estimate what that length looks like.

Direct students' attention to *Student Activity Book* page 2.

Let's each try it. Look at the items on this list. Think about the tools we have been using and the benchmarks we established and estimate the length.

Students record their estimates on *Student Activity Book* page 2. Have students put away the tools they were using to find benchmarks, but have them use one or two of the benchmarks to find the estimates. Tell students they will find the actual measurements in the following session, so they can leave the third column blank. Students work in pairs to estimate each of the lengths listed. Students record both their own and their partner's estimates. ❹

It is likely that students will come up with different estimates. They discuss with their partner why their estimates differ. ❺

Making good measurement estimates is hard and takes a great deal of practice. The purpose of this activity is to help students get a sense of what each unit looks like without relying on the tool itself. As students work, ask questions like:

Name		Date
Size, Shape, and Symmetry		

Using Measurement Benchmarks and Measurement Tools

Object	Estimate	Actual Measurement
Length of my pencil		
Width of my pencil		
Height of my desk from the floor		
Length of my notebook		
Width of the classroom window		
My teacher's height		

2   Unit 4   Sessions 1.1, 1.2

▲ **Student Activity Book, p. 2**

Will the length of the pencil be longer than one foot or shorter than one foot? Is it about half of one foot? Am I more than one yard tall? More than two yards? How can you tell?

ONGOING ASSESSMENT: Observing Students at Work

Students use their measurement benchmarks to estimate lengths of objects in their classroom.

- **Do students choose a reasonable benchmark to measure an object?**

- **Can students make fairly accurate estimates based on the benchmarks they choose?**

DIFFERENTIATION: Supporting the Range of Learners

Intervention If students are having difficulty estimating lengths with accuracy, encourage them to use a benchmark against the object they are measuring. If students are measuring the width of the window, they can place a book along the window for one or two iterations, or all along, until they begin to develop a sense of the length of a foot.

Students use an object they know to be about 1 foot in length to find the total length of the class white board.

Extension You may want to add some measurements for students who are making accurate estimates. Longer lengths can be more challenging to estimate so you may want to ask students to work on the length of the classroom or the length of the hall outside the classroom.

DISCUSSION

③ Why Do Our Measurements Differ?

10 MIN CLASS

Math Focus Points for Discussion

◆ Estimating lengths based on common units (centimeter, inch, foot, yard, meter)

Bring the students together after about 30 minutes, even if everyone did not get to each measurement.

Did you and your partner ever get different estimates for the same thing? Why do you think this happened?

Possible reasons include using benchmarks that are not the same size (for example, one may be a bit smaller than an inch and the other may be a bit larger than an inch), and using different strategies for approximating an estimate to the nearest unit or part of a unit.

SESSION FOLLOW-UP

④ Daily Practice and Homework

 Daily Practice: For ongoing review, have students complete *Student Activity Book* page 3.

 Homework: Using the questions on *Student Activity Book* page 4 to guide them, students talk to one or more adults to find at least four situations in which they measure. Students should look for situations in which people estimate and in which they use measurement tools for exact measures.

 Student Math Handbook: Students and families may use *Student Math Handbook* page 101–102 for reference and review. See pages 170–174 in the back of this unit.

 Family Letter: Send home copies of Family Letter (M9–M10).

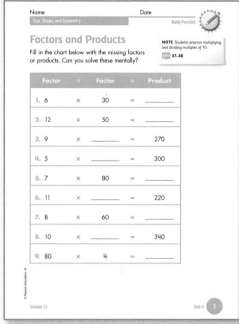

▲ **Student Activity Book, p. 3**

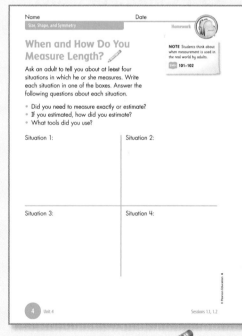

▲ **Student Activity Book, p. 4**

Measurement Tools

Math Focus Points

◆ Using U.S. standard and metric units to accurately measure length

◆ Determining when estimates or exact measurements are needed

Vocabulary

millimeter	kilometer
standard system	estimate
metric system	

Today's Plan		Materials
ACTIVITY **①Reading Measurement Tools**	15 MIN PAIRS	• Measurement Questions chart (or board)* • Rulers; yardsticks/metersticks
ACTIVITY **②Using Measurement Tools**	30 MIN PAIRS	• *Student Activity Book*, p. 2 (from Session 1.1)
DISCUSSION **③Estimate or Exact?**	15 MIN CLASS	• *Student Activity Book*, p. 4 (from Session 1.1) • Chart: "Exact vs. Estimated Measures"*; scissors
SESSION FOLLOW-UP **④Daily Practice and Homework**		• *Student Activity Book*, pp. 5–6 • M11–M12, Family Letter* • *Student Math Handbook*, pp. 101, 103

*See *Materials to Prepare*, p. 21.

Ten-Minute Math

Today's Number: Broken Calculator Students create five expressions that equal 2,600. They must use either addition or subtraction in their expressions. The 2 and 6 keys are broken. Have two or three students share their equations and explain how they know that the answer is correct. (Examples: $1,300 + 1,300 = 2,600$ or $3,700 - 1,000 - 55 - 45 = 2,600$)

ACTIVITY

Reading Measurement Tools

15 MIN   PAIRS

Distribute a ruler to each student and a yardstick/meterstick to each table (or group of three to four students). Review with them how to read measurement tools.

Can you find a **millimeter**? A centimeter? A foot? An inch? How many feet are in each yard? How many inches? . . . Can you use your meterstick to show how many millimeters in a centimeter? How many centimeters are in a meter?

Refer students to the questions that you listed on chart paper or on the board for this session:

• Which is larger, an inch or a centimeter?

• Which is larger, a meter or a yard?

• How many inches are between 7 and 11 on the ruler?

• How many millimeters are in one centimeter?

• How many millimeters are between 47 and 51 on the meterstick?

• What does the 90 on the meterstick mean?

• How many centimeters are in one meter?

Students take a few minutes to find the answer to each question with their partners. Then ask for a few students to share their answers and explain their reasoning with the class. Listen to determine whether students can identify the different measurement units and how they relate to the larger and smaller units. Ask more questions similar to the ones above if students need more practice.

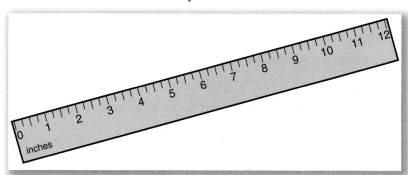

ONGOING ASSESSMENT: Observing Students at Work

Students examine measurement tools to become familiar with units and their relationship to one another.

- **Can students identify standard units of measure (e.g., millimeters, meters, inches, etc.)?**

- **Can they find some relationships among these tools?** (e.g., How many millimeters are in a meter? A millimeter is smaller than a centimeter, and so on)

ACTIVITY

30 MIN   PAIRS

② Using Measurement Tools

On the board, list the units of measure that students have been using (foot, meter, centimeter, inch, yard). Clarify the difference between U.S. standard and metric measurements.

We use two systems of measurement in the United States. Sometimes we use the U.S. standard system and other times we use the metric system. Do you know which of these units are metric units?

Most countries use only the metric system. Can anyone name one of these countries? Has anyone moved and needed to change measurement systems?

Many students will be familiar with metric measurement for length from measuring at school or perhaps hearing about 5- or 10-kilometer races. Make sure that students understand that you cannot mix these measurements when reporting a distance. (That is, while it is common to identify a measurement as 5 feet 2 inches, we do not identify a measurement as 1 foot 3 centimeters.)

Collect a few examples of each measurement that we all commonly see, such as these: road work 100 feet, the race is 10K (kilometers), rainfall for the month: 3.5 inches.

Students now measure the lengths of what they estimated in the previous session on *Student Activity Book* page 2. They record their measurements in the final column. If students get different measurements, they record them both.

Object	Estimate	Actual Measurement
Length of my pencil		
Width of my pencil	1cm	
Height of my desk from the floor	2 feet	
Length of my notebook		
Width of the classroom window	1 meter	
My teacher's height	2 meters or 5ft 10 inches	

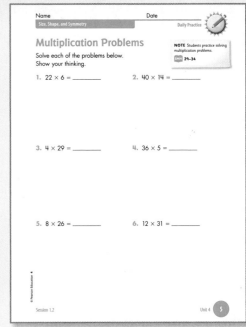

Name _____ Date _____

Size, Shape, and Symmetry   Daily Practice

Multiplication Problems

Solve each of the problems below.
Show your thinking.

NOTE Students practice solving multiplication problems.

29–34

1. 22 × 6 = _____   2. 40 × 14 = _____

3. 4 × 29 = _____   4. 36 × 5 = _____

5. 8 × 26 = _____   6. 12 × 31 = _____

Session 1.2   Unit 4 5

▲ Student Activity Book, p. 5

ONGOING ASSESSMENT: Observing Students at Work

Students find the exact measure of the objects they estimated in the previous session.

- **Can students accurately use measurement tools?** Do they line up the tools, make sure there is no space in between tools, place the proper end at the beginning of the object?

- **Can students accurately read measurement tools?**

DIFFERENTIATION: Supporting the Range of Learners

Intervention If students are making errors using their measurement tools, bring the group together to highlight accurate measurement practices and suggest strategies.

- I notice that Cheyenne is lining up her tools in a straight line along the table. What would happen if she left a gap?

- I see that Emaan is checking to make sure that the 0 on his ruler is lined up with the end of the object. What would happen if he had placed the ruler with the 12 or 1 lined up with the end of the object?

Extension If students finish quickly, identify other lengths in the classroom to measure.

Math Notes

❶ Estimate vs. Exact Measure While some measurements will be different because students have used a tool incorrectly, other differences in measurement will reflect the difficulty in being precise. For one person a particular length might be recorded as an inch, while another might seek more precision and report the measurement as 1 and $\frac{1}{8}$ inches. In daily usage, the purpose of a measurement is taken into account when determining how precise the measurement needs to be.

❷ Recording Measurements Students may record the same measurement in different ways depending on what unit or units they use. For instance, with metric units, $2\frac{1}{4}$ meters and 2 meters and 25 cm are the same measurement; with U.S. units $3\frac{1}{2}$ feet is the same as 3 feet and 6 inches. When such differences are noted, encourage students to use the tools to reason through each measurement to determine how the measurements are the same.

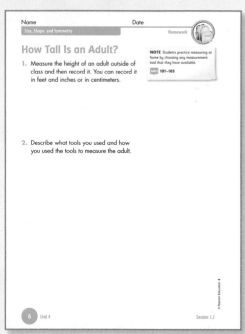

▲ Student Activity Book, p. 6

15 MIN   CLASS

DISCUSSION

③ Estimate or Exact?

Math Focus Points for Discussion

◆ Determining when estimates or exact measurements are needed

Refer students to the "Exact vs. Estimated Measures" chart that you prepared.❶

For the last 15 minutes of math class, have students cut out the boxes for each measurement situation they recorded on *Student Activity Book* page 4.❷

Collect at least one situation from each student, and post it in the appropriate column on the chart. Students may add the rest of their responses at a later time. As students post their responses, brainstorm other measurement situations and decide whether they would belong in the "Exact" or "Estimated" measures column.

SESSION FOLLOW-UP

④ Daily Practice and Homework

 Daily Practice: For ongoing review, have students complete *Student Activity Book* page 5.

 Homework: Students measure an adult's height on *Student Activity Book* page 6.

 Student Math Handbook: Students and families may use *Student Math Handbook* pages 101, 103 for reference and review. See pages 170–174 in the back of this unit.

 Family Letter: Send home copies of the Family Letter (M11–M12).

Assessment: How Long Is Our Classroom?

Math Focus Points

◆ Using U.S. standard and metric units to accurately measure length

◆ Finding perimeter using standard units

Vocabulary

perimeter

Today's Plan		Materials
1 DISCUSSION **Measuring Perimeter**	15 MIN · CLASS	• Rulers; yardsticks/metersticks; blank paper
2 ACTIVITY ***LogoPaths* Activity: Introducing *Missing Measures* (optional)**	GROUPS · CLASS	• Computers with *LogoPaths* software installed*
3 MATH WORKSHOP **Measuring Length** **3A** Perimeter Problems **3B** *LogoPaths* Activity: *Missing Measures* (optional) **3C** Assessment: How Long Is Our Classroom?	45 MIN	**3A** • *Student Activity Book,* pp. 7–8 **3B** • M1–M3* • Computers with *LogoPaths* software installed* **3C** • M8 ☑*; M13* • Rulers; yardsticks/metersticks
4 SESSION FOLLOW-UP **Daily Practice and Homework**		• *Student Activity Book,* pp. 9–10 • *Student Math Handbook,* pp. 103–105

*See *Materials to Prepare,* p. 21.

Ten-Minute Math

Today's Number: Broken Calculator Students create five expressions that equal 789. They must use both addition and subtraction in their expressions. The 7 key is broken. Have two or three students share their equations and explain how they know the answer is correct. (Examples: $989 - 300 + 100 = 789$ or $432 + 360 - 3 = 789$)

DISCUSSION

① Measuring Perimeter

Math Focus Points for Discussion

◆ Finding perimeter using standard units.

Students were introduced to the measure of perimeter in Grade 3 in the *Perimeter, Angles, and Area* unit and practiced finding the perimeter of many objects. Here, students review the concept of perimeter and ways to measure perimeter accurately.

We have been measuring the length of many objects, for example my desk. What would you measure if I asked you to measure the perimeter of my desk?

If students do not know that perimeter is the measure of the length of the outside edge of an object, explain that to them.

If an ant started in one corner and walked along the border of the entire desk, the total length would be the perimeter. Every shape has a perimeter: rectangles, triangles, circles, and every other shape that we can imagine.

Show students a sheet of letter-sized paper.

We are going to find the perimeter of this sheet of paper in inches. What would you estimate it to be?

Students might say:

"I think it will be about 3 feet because I know that two of the sides are each about 1 foot so that is 2 feet. And the other 2 sides look like they might make about 1 foot together. There are 12 inches in each foot and 3 × 12 = 36. So it is about 36 inches."

"I know the space between my thumb and my pinky when I stretch out my fingers is 5 inches. And when I put that around the paper I get to about 40."

"I don't need to estimate, because I know that the paper is $8\frac{1}{2}$ inches by 11 inches. So I added up all the sides in my head and got 39."

How would your answer change if you measured the same perimeter in centimeters? What would you estimate the answer to be? Would it be bigger or smaller than our answer in inches?

Allow students a few minutes to think about their new estimate. Focus on whether the measurement will be larger or smaller. Explain to students that one activity they will be working on in the Math Workshop is estimating and finding perimeters of objects in the classroom.❶

ACTIVITY

2 *LogoPaths* Activity: Introducing Missing Measures (optional)

GROUPS CLASS

In this version of the *Missing Measures LogoPaths* activity, students are given pictures of incomplete figures that include some dimensions.❷ ❸ They use the *LogoPaths* software to complete each figure and then find the perimeter of each.❹

In Grade 3, you learned a *LogoPaths* activity called *Missing Measures* where you used forward and backward moves and right and left turns of 90° to finish incomplete pictures of rectangles. In the Grade 4 version of this activity, you will use *LogoPaths* commands to finish pictures of rectangles and squares, but also other shapes with more than four sides. Some of these figures will have turns that are other multiples of 30 degrees, like 60 or 120. You used turns like these when you played *Feed the Turtle* in Grade 3.

Display the figure you prepared:

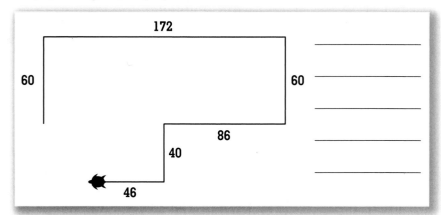

Your job is to use the clues you see on the incomplete figures like this one to write commands that will let the turtle finish each polygon.

First, you'll have to write commands to draw what's already shown and then the commands to finish the shape. What commands would you write to show what the turtle has drawn so far?

As students suggest commands, ask them to explain their suggestions. When students reach consensus, write the suggested commands on the lines next to the drawing. Be sure to use the appropriate *LogoPaths* abbreviations [**FORWARD (FD), BACK (BK), LEFT (LT), AND RIGHT (RT)**] and *no* commas between the commands, since commas are not used when entering these commands in the Command Center.

FD 60 RT 90 FD 172 RT 90

FD 60 RT 90 FD 86 LT 90

FD 40 RT 90 FD 46

Open the Free Explore option in the *LogoPaths* software and enter the commands that the class came up with in the Command Center. Use the Label Lengths tool to check that the side lengths of the figure on the computer match the side lengths of the figure you displayed.

What commands should we type now to help the turtle finish the shape?

Students might say:

 "The side on the top is 172 steps, so I added the 86 and 46 and got 132. Then I knew that the turtle had to go 40 more steps to finish the bottom."

 "The turtle has to turn right 90 degrees to finish the last side."

"I know the last side has to be 100 steps because I added the 60 and 40 from the other 2 sides that are vertical. So the turtle just has to go 40 steps to finish that side."

After all the new commands have been entered, use the **HT** command to hide the turtle so the students can see the full polygon. Then use the Teach Tool to name the set of commands. Let students know that their last task in this activity is to determine the perimeter of each polygon that they help the turtle complete.

MATH WORKSHOP

③ Measuring Length

45 MIN

For the remainder of this and the next two sessions, students work on three Math Workshop activities. One of these activities, How Long Is Our Classroom?, is an observed assessment.

Students find the perimeter of several objects, measure a length of their classroom, and use *LogoPaths* software (optional) to complete figures with missing dimensions and determine their perimeter. Distribute the materials and introduce the three tasks as explained below. Note that for How Long Is Our Classroom?, it is easier to get accurate measurements if only a small number of students work on this task at the same time. Thus, you may want to assign two to three pairs to begin with this task while all others begin working on the other two activities.

How Long Is Our Classroom? assesses students on Benchmark 1: Use appropriate measurement tools to measure distance. As students work on this activity in small groups of two or three, observe them as they plan and then measure the length across the classroom. Students will be working on the activity during the next two sessions, so you do not have to observe all of your students on the same day. See the directions below for more specific information about this assessment.

③A Perimeter Problems

INDIVIDUALS

Students estimate and measure the perimeter of the surface of several objects in their classroom on *Student Activity Book* pages 7–8. They choose one object and compare the measurement with two different units. (For example, they may measure the perimeter of the classroom door in yards and also in feet.)

As students work, ask questions like the following:

How did you make your estimate? Did you use a benchmark? How did it help you?

Did you use the measurement of one object to help you make an estimate of another? [For example: I see that the perimeter of the table is ten feet.] Did that knowledge help you make an estimate for the perimeter of the other table, which is a bit smaller?

If the table has a perimeter of ten feet, what do you think the measurement will be if you measure it in inches? Will it be a larger measurement or a smaller one?

Name _____ Date _____

Size, Shape, and Symmetry

Perimeter Problems (page 1 of 2)

1. Estimate, and then find the perimeter of the objects listed below. Choose your own objects for the blank spaces.

Object	Unit of Measure (inches, feet, yards, centimeters, or meters)	Estimate	Actual Measurement
Your classroom door			
Your teacher's desk			
The board			

Sessions 1.3, 1.4, 1.5   Unit 4   **7**

▲ **Student Activity Book, p. 7**

Name _____ Date _____

Size, Shape, and Symmetry

Perimeter Problems (page 2 of 2)

2. Choose one of your perimeter measurements. Estimate and measure it again using another unit.

3. Explain why the two measurements of the same perimeter are different.

8 Unit 4   Sessions 1.3, 1.4,

▲ **Student Activity Book, p. 8** *WRITING*

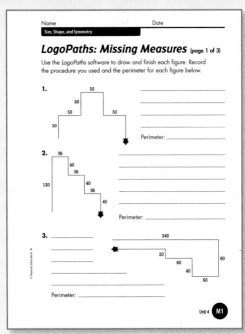

▲ Resource Masters, M1

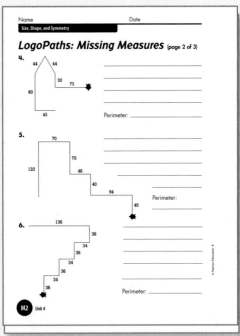

▲ Resource Masters, M2–M3

ONGOING ASSESSMENT: Observing Students at Work

Students measure the perimeter of several objects using different measurement units.

- **Can students identify and measure the perimeter of objects?**

- **Can students make a reasonable estimate of a measure?**

- **Do students know that the larger the unit of measure the smaller the total measurement will be?**

3B *LogoPaths* Activity: *Missing Measures* (optional)

INDIVIDUALS

Students work alone or with partners on this *LogoPaths* activity. They solve problems from *LogoPaths: Missing Measures* (M1–M3), where they are given pictures of incomplete figures that include some dimensions. They use the *LogoPaths* software to complete each figure and then determine its perimeter.

ONGOING ASSESSMENT: Observing Students at Work

Students complete figures with missing dimensions, using known dimensions, and determine the perimeter of the completed figures.

- **Can students use *LogoPaths* commands fluently?**

- **Do they use right and left turns consistently and correctly even when the turtle is not facing straight up?**

- **Are they able to determine the missing measures and turns from the given information?** For example, can they use the length of a side or combining line segments to determine the length of the parallel side? When the length of a parallel side is given, as in Problem 2 where the given length is 60, do they understand that the parallel line segments must be equal to that length?

- **Are they able to accurately determine the perimeter of each completed figure?**

3C Assessment: How Long Is Our Classroom?

INDIVIDUALS

Students measure the length of the classroom and record their findings on Assessment: How Long Is Our Classroom? (M13). Your directions to this activity will depend on the size, shape, and layout of your classroom.

Following are some guidelines to consider in setting up the task:

- If the length is along a wall, clearly mark the start and end points. You may want to choose a wall that has a small obstruction (a heater or bookcase). Students will then have to figure out how to measure the piece of the wall that is obstructed (and they must understand that the length does not include the measurement of the perimeter of these objects).

- You may want to place a piece of masking tape on the floor across the length or width of the classroom for students to measure.

- If there is no clear length in the classroom, you may want to have students measure any length that is long enough so that they pick up and place the meterstick several times.

Students have to figure out how to adjust measurements because of obstructions.

When you have explained the task to students, gather a few quick estimates and record them on the board.

This activity is an opportunity to assess your students' understanding and skill at measuring length. Do they use measurement tools appropriately and accurately? Can they keep track of their measurements as they work to measure a fairly long length? As students work, observe them in their small groups, and record your observations on Assessment Checklist: How Long Is Our Classroom? (M8). Students work on this activity over the next two sessions, allowing you several opportunities to observe all your students.

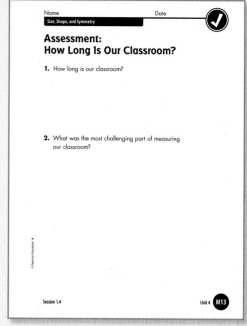

▲ Resource Masters, M13 PORTFOLIO

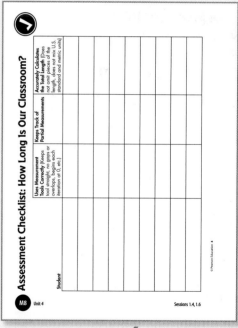

▲ Resource Masters, M8 ✓

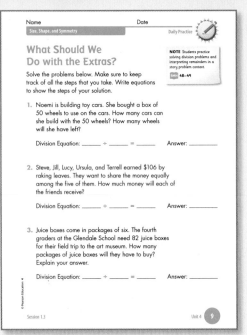

Student Activity Book, p. 9

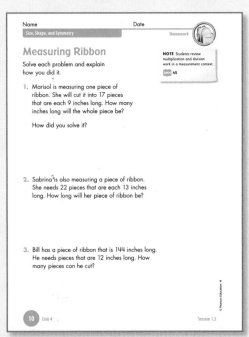

Student Activity Book, p. 10

ONGOING ASSESSMENT: Observing Students at Work

Students measure a length that is several iterations of a meterstick/ yardstick finding ways to keep track of their measurements.

- **Can students read the calibrations on the measuring tool correctly?**

- **Does the student position the measuring tool to get the most accurate measurements (i.e., leaves no gaps between the tool, places the tool in a straight line)?**

- **Can the students accurately keep track of the length and calculate the total measurement?**

- **Can students identify a measurement that is between two units?**

DIFFERENTIATION: Supporting the Range of Learners

Intervention This length may be challenging for some students. If a student is not yet familiar with accurate measurement practice, you may want to choose a shorter length and work with the student to line up the tool and read the tool properly.

SESSION FOLLOW-UP
4 Daily Practice and Homework

Daily Practice: For ongoing review, have students complete *Student Activity Book* page 9.

Homework: Students complete the multiplication and division word problems on *Student Activity Book* page 10.

Student Math Handbook: Students and families may use *Student Math Handbook* pages 103–105 for reference and review. See pages 170–174 in the back of this unit.

Measuring Length

Math Focus Points

◆ Using U.S. standard and metric units to accurately measure length

◆ Recognizing and explaining possible sources of measurement error

◆ Finding perimeter using standard units

◆ Comparing different paths that have the same length

Today's Plan	Materials
MATH WORKSHOP **① Measuring Length** 40 MIN **①A** Perimeter Problems **①B** *LogoPaths* Activity: *Missing Measures* (optional) **①C** Assessment: How Long Is Our Classroom? **①D** Mapping 100 Feet	**①A** • *Student Activity Book,* pp. 7–8 **①B** • M1–M3 (from Session 1.3) • Computers with *LogoPaths* software installed* **①C** • M8; M13 (from Session 1.3) • Rulers; yardsticks/metersticks **①D** • *Student Activity Book,* p. 11 • Masking tape; ruler; yardsticks/metersticks
DISCUSSION **② Why Are Our Measurements Different?** 20 MIN CLASS	• *Student Activity Book,* p. 12
SESSION FOLLOW-UP **③ Daily Practice**	• *Student Activity Book,* p. 13 • *Student Math Handbook,* pp. 103–105

*See *Materials to Prepare,* p. 21.

Ten-Minute Math

Today's Number: Broken Calculator Students create five expressions that equal 998. They must use only subtraction in their expressions. The 1 and 9 keys are broken. Have two or three students share their equations and explain how they know the answer is correct. (Examples: $3{,}000 - 2{,}002 = 998$ or $2{,}000 - 700 - 250 - 52 = 998$)

MATH WORKSHOP

Measuring Length

40 MIN

Students continue to work on activities to practice using U.S. standard and metric units to measure length. Continue to assess students as they work on Assessment: How Long Is Our Classroom? (M13). A new activity is added, Mapping 100 Feet. This new activity requires substantial space and organization and it is recommended that no more than two to three groups work on it at the same time.

1A Perimeter Problems

INDIVIDUALS

For complete details about this activity, see Session 1.3, page 37.

1B *LogoPaths* Activity: *Missing Measures* (optional)

INDIVIDUALS PAIRS

For complete details about this activity, see Session 1.3, pages 35–36.

1C Assessment: How Long Is Our Classroom?

GROUPS

For complete details about this activity, see Session 1.3, pages 38–39. Continue to assess students as they measure the length of the classroom, using Assessment Checklist: How Long Is Our Classroom? (M8) to record your observations. If students are having difficulty using measurement tools or keeping track of their measurements, have them continue to work on this activity until they are successful instead of going on to Mapping 100 Feet. Students should finish this activity before the discussion at the end of the session.

1D Mapping 100 Feet

GROUPS PAIRS

Mapping 100 Feet has proven to be an exciting activity for students. The distance is long and it is interesting for students to see the actual length of 100 feet. (There are not many adults who can accurately identify what a path of 100 feet looks like!) Students also get the chance to compare different paths and consider how a straight path can look like a much different distance than one with many turns and twists. But it is not necessary for all students to do this activity. Students should finish the other three activities before they move on to this and if they do not have time to do it, they will still benefit from the discussion.

For this activity, you may want to keep students inside the classroom. Or, if it is possible, you may want to allow them to measure a hallway or another distance outside the classroom.

In pairs or groups, students plan out a path that is 100 feet long. They will need to make several decisions:

- Where will the path begin?

- How will they measure the path? Students may decide to use rulers, especially if the path has many bends or twists. But they may also use a yardstick, realizing that this is equal to three feet. If a group does not notice this, ask them whether there is another tool that they could use that may help them keep track of the distance.

- How will they mark the path? Students may use tape to mark the beginning or the end of the path and make a drawing of the path as they go along. Or they may use masking tape to mark every 10 feet so others can follow their path.

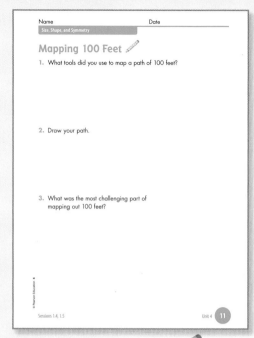

Students plan a path 100 feet long.

When students are finished, they fill in *Student Activity Book* page 11.

ONGOING ASSESSMENT: Observing Students at Work

Students work in pairs or groups to create a path that is 100 feet long.

- **Do students have a sense of how long this path will be (i.e., do they begin working on a distance and realize that it is much less than or much more than 100 feet)?**

▲ **Student Activity Book, p. 11**

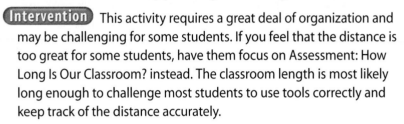

• **Do students position the measuring tool to get the most accurate measurements (i.e., leaving no gaps between the tool and placing the tools in a straight line)?**

• **Can students accurately keep track of the length and calculate the total measurement?**

DIFFERENTIATION: Supporting the Range of Learners

Intervention This activity requires a great deal of organization and may be challenging for some students. If you feel that the distance is too great for some students, have them focus on Assessment: How Long Is Our Classroom? instead. The classroom length is most likely long enough to challenge most students to use tools correctly and keep track of the distance accurately.

Extension If a group or pair of students finishes this task quickly and easily, challenge them to find the perimeter of the classroom. Or challenge them to create an alternate path that is 100 feet long and looks quite different than the one they created.

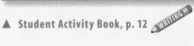

▲ Student Activity Book, p. 12

DISCUSSION

2 Why Are Our Measurements Different?

20 MIN CLASS

Math Focus Points for Discussion

◆ Recognizing and explaining possible sources of measurement error

After most of the class has measured the classroom, have students write their measurements of the classroom on the board or post them on self-stick notes on the board. Briefly compare the actual measurements with the estimates that were made before students started measuring. You may want to ask students what benchmarks they used to estimate (e.g., "I know that I am 4 and a half feet tall. I pictured myself lying down across the room and thought it would take about four of me").

First, allow students about ten minutes to work in pairs on *Student Activity Book* page 12. Students continue to work in the same pairs, discussing answers with their partners, but writing answers on their own sheets.

Bring students together to ask the following questions:

Why do you think all of our measurements are not the same?

Collect a few examples of students' ideas. Possible reasons for getting larger measurements include placing the meterstick incorrectly so they overlap, placing a meterstick so that it zigzags across the distance, or making a mistake in the total calculation. Possible reasons for getting a smaller measurement include placing the meterstick incorrectly so that there are gaps between each meter measured, incorrectly estimating a piece that cannot be directly measured, or making a mistake in the total calculation.

What are some things we want to remember about measuring?

Record some of the points students have made or ask for more. If some of the points mentioned above have not been suggested, ask a question that points out the error (e.g., "Which distance do you think is longer, a straight line across this room or a zigzag line across the room?"). Draw a picture to illustrate this point.

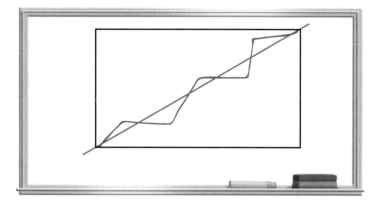

Record these guidelines for measuring on the board or on chart paper.

Guidelines for Measuring

—Don't mix metric and standard units.

—Hold the ruler straight against the thing you are measuring.

—Mark where the ruler ends with your finger, and then move the ruler and start it at your finger. You could use a pencil instead of your finger.

—Make sure you start measuring at 0.

—Write down each time you put the ruler down so you don't lose track.

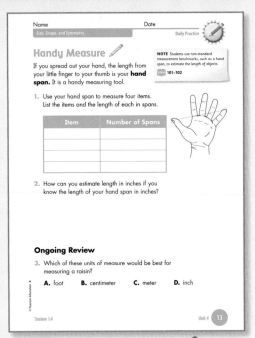

Student Activity Book, p. 13

Remind students that they have one more day to return to these measuring activities in the next session.

3 Daily Practice

Daily Practice: For reinforcement of this unit's content, have students complete *Student Activity Book* page 13.

Student Math Handbook: Students and families may use *Student Math Handbook* pages 103–105 for reference and review. See pages 170–174 in the back of the unit.

Measuring Length,
continued

Math Focus Points

◆ Using U.S. standard and metric units to accurately measure length

◆ Finding perimeter using standard units

◆ Comparing different paths that have the same length

Today's Plan		Materials
MATH WORKSHOP **❶ Measuring Length** **1A Perimeter Problems** **1B** *LogoPaths* Activity: *Missing Measures* (optional) **1C Mapping 100 Feet**	🕐 45 MIN	**1A** • *Student Activity Book,* pp. 7–8 **1B** • M1–M3 (from Session 1.3) • Computers with *LogoPaths* software installed* **1C** • *Student Activity Book,* p. 11 • Masking tape; rulers; yardsticks/metersticks
DISCUSSION **❷ Mapping 100 Feet**	🕐 15 MIN 👥 CLASS	• Rulers; yardsticks/metersticks
SESSION FOLLOW-UP **❸ Daily Practice**		• *Student Activity Book,* p. 14 • *Student Math Handbook,* pp. 101–105

*See *Materials to Prepare,* p. 21.

Ten-Minute Math

Today's Number: Broken Calculator Students create five expressions that equal 1,550. They must use both addition and subtraction in their expressions. The 1 and 5 keys are broken. Have two or three students share their equations and explain how they know the answer is correct. (Examples: 3,000 − 2,000 + 600 − 30 − 20 = 1,550 or 2,000 − 600 + 240 − 90 = 1,550)

MATH WORKSHOP
① Measuring Length

45 MIN

Students continue to work on activities to practice using U.S. standard and metric units to measure length. If there are a few students who still need to be assessed on the activity How Long Is Our Classroom?, have them finish this instead of going on to Mapping 100 Feet.

①A Perimeter Problems

INDIVIDUALS

For complete details about this activity, see Session 1.3, page 37.

①B *LogoPaths* Activity: *Missing Measures* (optional)

INDIVIDUALS PAIRS

For complete details about this activity, see Session 1.3, pages 35–36.

①C Mapping 100 Feet

GROUPS PAIRS

For complete details about this activity, see Session 1.4, pages 42–43.

DISCUSSION
② Mapping 100 Feet

15 MIN CLASS

Math Focus Points for Discussion

◆ Comparing different paths that have the same length

Ask three or four groups of students to share their paths of 100 feet. Choose groups that created very different looking paths (long and straight versus paths with many turns). It is interesting for students to see that 100 feet stretched out may look quite different from a path with several shorter lines that travels around several curves.

Groups should have two to three minutes to share how they created their path, how they calculated the measurement, and whether there were any surprises about their path (Did they expect 100 feet to be longer or shorter?).

Allow the paths to remain on the floor for as long as possible so students can walk one another's paths for the next few days.

SESSION FOLLOW-UP
3 Daily Practice

Daily Practice: For reinforcement of this unit's content, have students complete *Student Activity Book* page 14.

Student Math Handbook: Students and families may use *Student Math Handbook* pages 101–105 for reference and review. See pages 170–174 in the back of this unit.

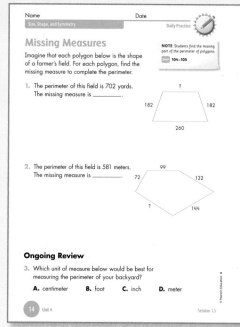

▲ **Student Activity Book, p. 14**

Mathematical Emphasis

Features of Shape Describing and classifying
2-dimensional figures

Math Focus Points

◆ Defining polygons as closed figures with line segments as sides,
and vertices

◆ Classifying polygons by attribute, including number of sides, length
of sides, and size of angles

◆ Combining polygons to make new polygons

◆ Recognizing number of sides as a descriptor of various polygons

◆ Developing vocabulary to describe attributes and properties of
quadrilaterals

◆ Understanding the relationship between squares and rectangles

Polygons of Many Types

		Student Activity Book	Student Math Handbook	Professional Development: Read Ahead of Time	
SESSION 2.1	p. 54				
Is It a Polygon? Students categorize shapes as polygons or not polygons. They discuss the attributes of polygons.		15–17	106	• **Dialogue Box:** Describing Polygons, p. 164 • **Part 4: Ten-Minute Math** in *Implementing Investigations in Grade 4:* Quick Images	
SESSION 2.2	p. 60				
Making Polygons Students use Power Polygons to make polygons that fit given descriptions.		18–21	106–107		
SESSION 2.3	p. 66				
Sorting Polygons Students sort polygons according to a variety of criteria, and continue to construct polygons. They use Logo-Paths software to draw rectangles with perimeters of 600 steps (optional).		18–20, 22–28	107	• **Teacher Note:** Beyond Vocabulary, p. 154	
SESSION 2.4	p. 74				
Sorting Quadrilaterals Students sort quadrilaterals according to a variety of criteria, and continue to construct polygons. They discuss the properties of quadrilaterals.		18–19, 23–24, 29–33	108–110		
SESSION 2.5	p. 80				
Assessment: What Is a Quadrilateral? Students discuss the relationship between squares and rectangles. They are assessed on their knowledge of quadrilaterals.		18–19, 22–24, 34–36	108–109	• **Teacher Note:** Classification of Quadrilaterals, p. 155 • **Dialogue Box:** Are Squares Rectangles?, p. 166 • **Teacher Note:** Assessment: What Is a Quadrilateral?, p. 156	

Ten-Minute Math See page 16 for an overview.

Quick Images: 2-D

- **T42–T43**, *Quick Images: 2-D* 📠 Cut apart images along dotted lines, and set aside images 1–10 for this investigation.

Materials to Gather	Materials to Prepare
• **T45, Polygons, Not Polygons** 📠 • **Power Polygons** (2 sets) • **Pie plates or plastic containers** (optional)	• **M18, Power Polygons** Make copies. • **Chart paper** Prepare two charts. On one chart, place a large circle labeled "Polygons" and the space outside the circle "Not Polygons." On the other chart, make two columns, one with the heading "A polygon *must* have . . ." and the other "A polygon *cannot* have . . ."
• **Power Polygons** (2 sets, distributed evenly among groups) • **Pie plates or plastic containers** (optional) • **Blank transparencies** (as needed)	
• **Power Polygons** (2 sets) • **Scissors, envelopes**	• **M19–M20, Shape Cards** Make copies and cut apart. (1 set per pair and 1 teacher set) • **M4, *LogoPaths: 600 Steps, Rectangles*** Make copies. (1 per student; optional) • **Chart paper** Label the chart paper "Names for Polygons." Create three columns titled "Number of Sides," "Name of Polygon," and "Words with the Same Prefix." • **Computers with *LogoPaths* software installed (optional)**
• **Power Polygons** (2 sets) • **M19–M20, Shape Cards** (1 set per pair and 1 teacher set; from Session 2.3)	• **M4, *LogoPaths: 600 Steps, Rectangles*** Make copies. (optional; from Session 2.3) • **Chart paper** Prepare a chart with two columns, one titled "All Quadrilaterals . . ." and the other titled "Some Quadrilaterals . . ." • **Computers with *LogoPaths* software installed (optional)**
• **M19–M20, Shape Cards** (1 set per pair and 1 teacher set; from Session 2.3) • **Power Polygons** (shapes A and C; 1 each per pair) • **Power Polygons** (2 sets)	• **M4, *LogoPaths: 600 Steps, Rectangles*** Make copies. (optional; from Session 2.3) • **M21, Assessment: What Is a Quadrilateral?** Make copies. (1 per student) • **M5, *LogoPaths: 800 Steps, Rectangles*** Make copies. • **Computers with *LogoPaths* software installed (optional)**

📠 Overhead Transparency

Is It a Polygon?

Math Focus Points

- Defining polygons as closed figures with line segments as sides, and vertices
- Classifying polygons by attribute, including number of sides, length of sides, and size of angles

Today's Plan		Materials
ACTIVITY ❶ **Polygons, Not Polygons**	20 MIN · PAIRS	• T45 • *Student Activity Book,* pp. 15–16
DISCUSSION ❷ **What Is a Polygon?**	20 MIN · CLASS	• *Student Activity Book,* p. 16 (completed, from Activity 1) • Chart: "Polygons/Not Polygons"* • Chart: "A polygon must have .../A polygon cannot have ..." *
ACTIVITY ❸ ***Guess My Rule* with Power Polygons**	20 MIN · CLASS · GROUPS	• M18* • Power Polygons; pie plates or plastic containers (optional)
SESSION FOLLOW-UP ❹ **Daily Practice**		• *Student Activity Book,* p. 17 • *Student Math Handbook,* p. 106

*See *Materials to Prepare,* p. 53.

Ten-Minute Math

NOTE: The Ten-Minute Math activity for this Investigation, *Quick Images: 2-D,* is not formally introduced, but is a variation of the activity *Quick Images,* which was introduced in *Factors, Multiples, and Arrays.* For a full description of the activity, see Part 4: Ten-Minute Math in *Implementing Investigations in Grade 4:* Quick Images.

Quick Images: 2-D Show Images 1 and 2 (one at a time) from *Quick Images: 2-D* (T42) and follow the procedure for the basic routine. For each image, students discuss how they drew their figures, including any revisions they made after each viewing.

Ask students:

- How did you remember the parts of the image?
- What did you notice about the relationship of the parts of the image?
- What helped you remember the whole image, so you could draw your design?

Polygons, Not Polygons

⏰ **20 MIN** 👥 **PAIRS**

Begin by displaying Polygons, Not Polygons (T45), on the overhead. Direct students' attention to the same sheet in *Student Activity Book* page 15.

Look at this set of shapes. The shapes at the top are called "**polygons.**" The shapes at the bottom are not. Talk to a partner about how the top three are alike and how they are different from the shapes at the bottom.

Give students a few minutes to talk with one another and then collect their ideas.

Now turn students' attention to *Student Activity Book* page 16.

Talk with your partner about each of the shapes on this sheet. When you agree that one is or is not a polygon write P or NP on the shape. If you can't agree, put a question mark next to the shape.

As you circulate around the classroom, listen for whether students notice that the figures that are polygons are all closed shapes with straight lines that do not cross each other.

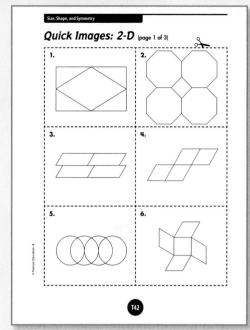

▲ **Transparencies, T42** 🖨

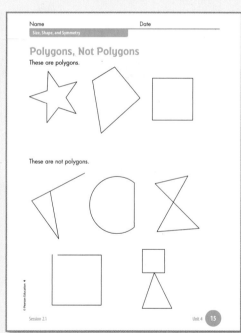

▲ **Student Activity Book, p. 15; Resource Masters, M17; T45** 🖨

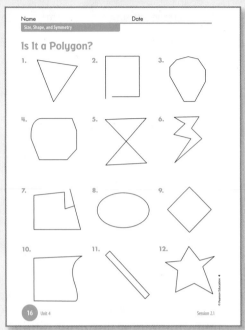

ONGOING ASSESSMENT: Observing Students at Work

Students examine a set of shapes and determine which are polygons and which are not.

- **Are students articulating properties such as: it has to be closed, it has to have line segments for sides, the sides cannot cross?**

- **Are students identifying shapes that are less familiar (such as shape 3 or shape 6) as polygons?**

DIFFERENTIATION: Supporting the Range of Learners

Intervention For students having difficulty, focus their attention on just two of the shapes. Point to two of the polygons and ask them to tell you what is the same about them. Have them write the phrases they use. Then point to one of the nonpolygons and one of the polygons and ask the students to tell you how they are different from one another. Write their phrases, so that they will have their own descriptors to call upon.

DISCUSSION

2 What Is a Polygon?

20 MIN   CLASS

Math Focus Points for Discussion

◆ Defining polygons as closed figures with line segments as sides, and vertices

Display the chart you prepared with the labels "Polygons" and "Not Polygons."

Tell students that they are going to play a silent game called Place the Shape. One at a time, a student from each pair comes to the chart to draw one of the shapes from *Student Activity Book* page 16. They draw the shape inside the circle if they think it is a polygon, or outside the circle if they think it is not a polygon.

When a shape is drawn, we will all think about it without saying anything. Is it in the right place? When it's your turn, if there is a shape you think is in the wrong place, you may place a question mark next to that shape instead of drawing a new one.

To emphasize the game's silence, you might use hand gestures to indicate turns instead of calling names.

Once all the shapes have been placed, allow some time to discuss any shapes that were questioned. Students should offer their reasons and explanations for any shape they challenge. If there are shapes misplaced that have not been questioned, bring them up yourself by asking:

I am wondering if anyone has anything to say about shape _____?

At the end of this discussion the shapes should be arranged like this:

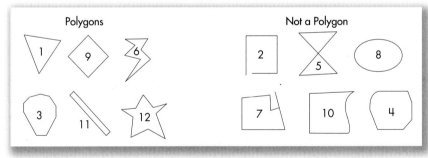

Show students the chart you prepared with the headings "A polygon must have . . . " and "A polygon cannot have . . ."

Let's write some of your ideas about polygons. For a shape to be a polygon, what must be true? What makes a shape not a polygon?

List students' ideas on the chart. These should include the following:

- Polygons have straight lines (line segments) for sides, which intersect only at the endpoints or vertices.

- Polygons cannot have curved sides, sides that cross each other, or sides that do not meet.❶

Teaching Notes

❷ Power Polygons The set of Power Polygon pieces includes the six pattern block shapes and nine other related polygons. In this unit, students use the Power Polygon pieces to build polygons, to study angle size, and to measure area. Like the pattern blocks, the Power Polygons are actually three-dimensional objects that are used to study two-dimensional shapes by focusing on one of the faces. For this purpose, the Power Polygon that matches the yellow pattern block is called a hexagon even though it is really a hexagonal prism.

❸ Distributing Power Polygons Decide how you will distribute the two sets evenly among small groups of three or four students, perhaps by putting handfuls of each color (which includes several shapes), in pie plates or plastic containers. When students are working with their small group's set of Power Polygons, let them know that if they need more of a particular shape they may borrow from another group's set.

Differentiation

❹ English Language Learners To ensure that English Language Learners know the vocabulary necessary to discuss polygons, you can preview this game by playing a modified version. First, review key terms such as *side* and *angle*. Then say a rule such as "It has three sides." Have students put two polygons that *fit* the rule on a piece of paper and one that *does not fit the rule* off the paper. Repeat with various rules until you think English Language Learners are confident with the vocabulary. Finally, have students come up with rules for each other to guess while they practice playing the actual game.

ACTIVITY

20 MIN   CLASS   GROUPS

③ *Guess My Rule* with Power Polygons

Do you remember building designs with pattern blocks? For this unit we are going to be using a set of plastic shapes called Power Polygons. The Power Polygons include all the shapes from the pattern block set as well as some new shapes. What do you notice about them?

Distribute a set of the Power Polygons to each small group.❷ ❸ The handout Power Polygons (M18) provides an illustration of all the shapes in the Power Polygon set.

Give students five minutes to look at the set of Power Polygons and then solicit two or three comments about the pieces. Students' comments might include that some are triangles, some are the same as the pattern blocks, or that some are quadrilaterals. Then introduce *Guess My Rule.*

Today you will play *Guess My Rule* with the Power Polygons. You may remember other versions of *Guess My Rule.* In this version, one person thinks of a rule and *without telling anyone the rule,* puts two of the Power Polygons that fit the rule on a piece of paper and one that does not fit off the paper. The other players then choose polygons to place as "fits the rule" or "does not fit the rule." Once you think you know what the rule is, you can say you want to tell the rule.❹

Choose a rule, such as "has right angles," and without telling students the rule, place two polygon pieces that fit this rule on the overhead, along with one polygon that does not fit. Play a round of *Guess My Rule* with the class to familiarize them with this version of the game. Students then work in small groups to play *Guess My Rule* with the Power Polygons. Each group will need a sheet of paper to place their polygons that "fit the rule."

Students will continue to play variations of *Guess My Rule* with polygons in Math Workshop in Sessions 2.3, 2.4, and 2.5.

As you observe students playing *Guess My Rule,* notice which attributes of the shapes they are paying attention to as they make their rules.

Students have had enough experience with triangles and quadrilaterals in earlier grades to have some ideas about the attributes of these polygons, including how they can be described by side length and angle size. Some rules that you might see students using include these:

- Have four sides/three sides/five sides, etc.

- Have sides that are all the same size

- Have angles that are all the same size

- Have angles that are different sizes

- Have no right angles

ONGOING ASSESSMENT: Observing Students at Work

Students sort polygons by various attributes: number of sides, side length, and angle size.

- **What attributes do students pay attention to as they make their rules?** Do these include number of sides, side length, and angle size? Do students consider orientation an attribute (i.e., they consider a triangle that sits on its base a different shape from a triangle that has no horizontal sides)?

- **Do students recognize common polygons, such as triangles and quadrilaterals?** Do they classify all 3-sided polygons as triangles? Do they distinguish between types of quadrilaterals, such as those with right angles and those without?

SESSION FOLLOW-UP

Daily Practice

 Daily Practice: For reinforcement of this unit's content, have students complete *Student Activity Book* page 17.

 Student Math Handbook: Students and parents may use *Student Math Handbook* page 106 for reference and review. See pages 170–174 in the back of this unit.

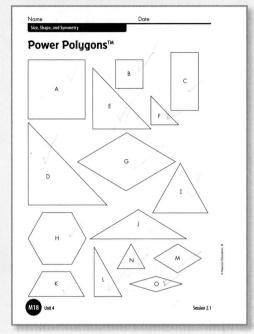

▲ Resource Masters, M18; T46

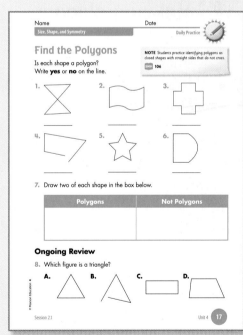

▲ Student Activity Book, p. 17

Making Polygons

Math Focus Points

- Combining polygons to make new polygons
- Recognizing number of sides as a descriptor of various polygons

Vocabulary

trapezoid
equilateral triangle
parallelogram
hexagon

Today's Plan		Materials
ACTIVITY **1 Introducing Making Polygons**	10 MIN · CLASS · GROUPS	• Power Polygons; pie plates or plastic containers (optional); blank transparencies
ACTIVITY **2 Making Polygons**	40 MIN · CLASS · GROUPS	• *Student Activity Book*, pp. 18–19 • Power Polygons
ACTIVITY **3 Introducing Names for Polygons**	10 MIN · CLASS · GROUPS	• *Student Activity Book*, p. 20 • Transparencies of traced polygons (from Activity 1)
SESSION FOLLOW-UP **4 Daily Practice**		• *Student Activity Book*, p. 21 • *Student Math Handbook*, pp. 106–107

Ten-Minute Math

Quick Images: 2-D Show Images 3 and 4 (one at a time) from *Quick Images: 2-D* (T42) and follow the procedure for the basic routine. For each image, students discuss how they drew their figures, including any revisions they made after each viewing.

Ask students:

- How did you remember the parts of the image?
- What did you notice about the relationship of the parts of the image?
- What helped you remember the whole image, so you could draw your design?

ACTIVITY

1 Introducing Making Polygons

In this session, students use Power Polygons to create new polygons with different numbers of sides. To demonstrate, place shapes K (trapezoid) and N (equilateral triangle) on the overhead. Ask students to find these shapes in their set.

How can you arrange these two polygons so the outline of the final shape they make is also a polygon?

Give students a minute to work on this problem. There are several ways to make new polygons with these two shapes, including:

It is also possible to make new polygons with these two shapes without having sides from each of the original polygons line up exactly. For example, the following is a seven-sided polygon:

Have a few students show their arrangements on the overhead. Be sure that the three in the illustration above (triangle, parallelogram, and hexagon) were shown, but include one or two examples of a seven-sided polygon if any student has created one. Each time a student has arranged the pieces to make a polygon, trace around the pieces and remove them. Use a dotted line to show the interior line segments and place the letters K and N to show how the polygon was made.

Ask students how many sides each polygon has. (For the three polygons in the first illustration on the previous page, the answers are 3, 4, and 6.) If some students include the interior line segments as sides, (for instance, reporting for the parallelogram as 5), trace the outline of the shape to draw their attention to the four sides (for the parallelogram). Be sure students understand that each side goes from vertex to vertex, even though one side might be made up of two sides of the two original polygons.

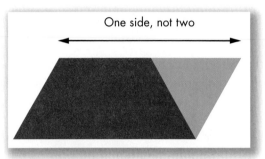

How can you arrange shapes K and N so that the outline they make will not be a polygon?

After a student has shown a way to do this, trace the outline and remove the pieces. One possibility might look like this:

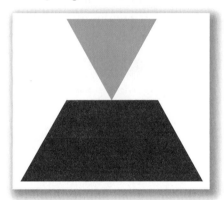

Why isn't this a polygon?

Have a few students offer their reasons. Students should recognize that this shape is still two distinct polygons, not one, each with its own set of sides and vertices.

ACTIVITY

② Making Polygons

40 MIN   CLASS   GROUPS

Students work in small groups, combining two or more Power Polygons (which could include copies of the same polygon) to make up other polygons, based on the directions on *Student Activity Book* pages 18–19. Students make polygons with 3, 4, 5, and 6 sides. Once they have made a polygon, they trace the outline, draw dotted lines to show the interior line segments, and place the letter identifying the Power Polygon inside the shape.

Students use Power Polygons to make and trace polygons with different numbers of sides.

You can start by making polygons that are familiar, but you should also challenge yourself and each other to make some polygons that are different from one another.

Students will have about 40 minutes to work on this activity in this session, which may not be long enough for all students to finish the student sheet. Let them know that they will have more time to work on this in Math Workshop in the next session.

✔ ONGOING ASSESSMENT: Observing Students at Work

Students construct polygons of various shapes, with different numbers of sides.

- **Can students combine two or more polygons to make a new shape that is a closed figure?**

- **Do students trace around the outside edge of the polygonal shapes and correctly count the number of sides?**

Name   Date

Size, Shape, and Symmetry

Making Polygons (page 1 of 2)

Follow these directions to make new polygons from two or more Power Polygons. Trace each new polygon. Draw dotted lines to show the sides of the Power Polygons™ that you used and write the letter of each Power Polygon inside.

1. Make 3 three-sided shapes. Make them as different from one another as you can.

2. Make 3 four-sided shapes. Make them as different from one another as you can.

18 Unit 4   Sessions 2.2, 2.3, 2.4, 2.5

▲ **Student Activity Book, p. 18**

Name   Date

Size, Shape, and Symmetry

Making Polygons (page 2 of 2)

Follow these directions to make new polygons from two or more Power Polygons. Trace each new polygon. Draw dotted lines to show the sides of the Power Polygons that you used and write the letter of each Power Polygon inside.

3. Make 2 different five-sided shapes.

4. Make 2 different six-sided shapes.

Sessions 2.2, 2.3, 2.4, 2.5   Unit 4 **19**

▲ **Student Activity Book, p. 19**

Math Notes

❶ Nonregular Polygons Some students may be startled when you call a nonregular polygon by the same name used for a regular polygon. For example, they may think that a hexagon has to have six equal sides and six equal angles. Explain that the name of any polygon tells only how many sides it has. Any polygon with four sides is a quadrilateral. All triangles have three sides. To identify a polygon that has equal sides and equal angles, we call it a regular polygon.

❷ Concave and Convex It is likely that some students' examples of hexagons will be concave (having the appearance of being "bent-in", which occurs when one or more interior angles is greater than 180 degrees) rather than *convex* (a shape with all interior angles less than 180 degrees). Students tend to recognize *convex* polygons as more familiar than concave ones, so it helps to expand their understanding of the mathematical properties of polygons so that students recognize both kinds. As students construct more polygons in this investigation, you may decide to introduce the terms *concave* and *convex* as they are describing different shapes; what is more important, however, is that they recognize that these are all polygons.

Convex hexagon   Concave hexagon

DIFFERENTIATION: Supporting the Range of Learners

Intervention For students who find the full set of polygons overwhelming, it may be helpful to reduce the number of Power Polygons for them to consider. One smaller set might be A, C, E, G, and L. Shifting the focus of the task can also be a way to simplify the work. Rather than focusing on producing a final polygon with a specific number of sides, have them arrange two or three of the power polygon pieces into a polygon and then determine the number of sides for that polygon.

ACTIVITY

③ Introducing Names for Polygons

10 MIN   CLASS   GROUPS

Bring the class together and show the tracings of the three polygons you made at the beginning of the session (triangle, parallelogram, and hexagon).

Ask students to name each of these polygons. Students should not have trouble naming the triangle or the quadrilateral, which some may remember is also called a parallelogram. Students may not know how to name the third shape, however.❶ If so, ask:

Let's count how many sides this polygon has . . . What other 6-sided shape have you seen before?

Students are likely to bring up the regular hexagon that they know from the pattern block set. Build a regular hexagon using two of the trapezoid pieces K on the overhead. Ask students to count the number of sides.

*One of these hexagons is familiar to you. The other is not as familiar, but it still has 6 sides. The word hexagon actually means "6 sides"— hexa means "6," and gon means "sides." So both of these figures are hexagons—they both have 6 sides. Can someone show us another hexagon that you made today?*❷

Collect a couple of examples of hexagons students made for Problem 4.

Ask students to look at *Student Activity Book* page 20.

Polygons are named by how many sides they have. *Poly* and *gon* are from the Greek language meaning "many" and "sides." This chart lists the names for polygons with sides that number from 3 to 12. Some of the words might sound odd, but parts of the words might sound familiar. The first part of the words that are used for naming polygons is related to the number of sides. For example, listen to the word for an 8-sided polygon, *octagon.* Does the beginning of the word *octagon* remind you of anything?

Some students might offer "octopus" and suggest that an octopus has eight legs. They may write this in the third column on their student sheets to get them started.

The first part of each of these words is called a *prefix.* For *octagon* the prefix is *oct* and that is also the beginning of *octopus.* Your job for homework tonight is to think about other words you know that have prefixes like the names of these polygons. Ask people at home to help you think of these, and we'll collect some of them tomorrow.❸

SESSION FOLLOW-UP

4 Daily Practice

Daily Practice: For ongoing review, have students complete *Student Activity Book* page 21.

  Student Math Handbook: Students and parents may use *Student Math Handbook* pages 106–107 for reference and review. See pages 170–174 in the back of this unit.

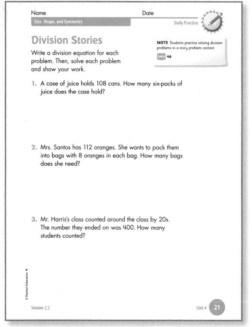

▲ **Student Activity Book, p. 21**

Differentiation

❸ **English Language Learners** For some English Language Learners, especially those who speak Spanish or French, the prefixes might be the same or similar in their native languages. Encourage these students to think of relevant words from their native languages. English Language Learners will transfer this knowledge to their learning of English vocabulary. When collecting students' answers the next day, encourage English Language Learners to share their native language words with the class.

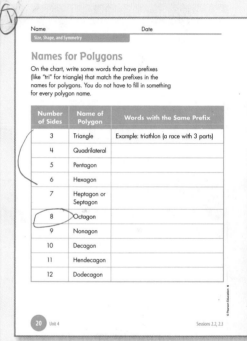

Names for Polygons

On the chart, write some words that have prefixes (like "tri" for triangle) that match the prefixes in the names for polygons. You do not have to fill in something for every polygon name.

Number of Sides	Name of Polygon	Words with the Same Prefix
3	Triangle	Example: triathlon (a race with 3 parts)
4	Quadrilateral	
5	Pentagon	
6	Hexagon	
7	Heptagon or Septagon	
8	Octagon	
9	Nonagon	
10	Decagon	
11	Hendecagon	
12	Dodecagon	

▲ **Student Activity Book, p. 20**

Sorting Polygons

Math Focus Points

◆ Recognizing number of sides as a descriptor of various polygons

◆ Classifying polygons by attribute, including number of sides, length of sides, and size of angles

◆ Combining polygons to make new polygons

Vocabulary
side
angle
right angle
parallel

Today's Plan		Materials
DISCUSSION ① **Names for Polygons**	10 MIN CLASS	• *Student Activity Book,* p. 20 (completed, from Session 2.2) • Chart: "Name for Polygons"*
ACTIVITY ② *LogoPaths* **Activity: Introducing 600 Steps** (optional)	CLASS GROUPS	• Computers with *LogoPaths* software installed*
MATH WORKSHOP ③ **Working with Polygons** 3A *Guess My Rule* with Shape Cards 3B Making Polygons 3C *LogoPaths Activity: 600 Steps* (optional)	50 MIN	**3A** • M19–M20* • *Student Activity Book,* p. 22 • Scissors; envelopes **3B** • *Student Activity Book,* pp. 18–19 (from Session 2.2); pp. 23–24 • Power Polygons **3C** • M4* • Computers with *LogoPaths* software installed*
SESSION FOLLOW-UP ④ **Daily Practice and Homework**		• *Student Activity Book,* pp. 25–28 • *Student Math Handbook,* p. 107

*See *Materials to Prepare,* p. 53.

Ten-Minute Math

Quick Images: 2-D   Show Images 5 and 6 (one at at time) from *Quick Images: 2-D* (T42) and follow the procedure for the basic routine. For each image, students discuss how they drew their figures, including any revisions they made after each viewing.

Ask students:

• How did you remember the parts of the image?

• What did you notice about the relationship of the parts of the image?

• What helped you remember the whole image, so you could draw your design?

DISCUSSION

①Names for Polygons

Math Focus Points for Discussion

◆ Recognizing number of sides as a descriptor of various polygons

Begin this session by having students share some of the words with prefixes that match those in the names for polygons, which they collected for homework. Show the chart you prepared, titled "Names for Polygons."

Today we are going to begin filling in our "Names for Polygons" chart. What are some of the words that you found?

Collect one or two words for each category on the "Names for Polygons" chart, if possible. Each time a word is added, ask students to tell how the meaning of the word is related to the name of the polygon. For example:

[Anna], you found the word *hendecasyllabic* in the dictionary—that's quite a word! How does it fit with hendecagon, which is a polygon with 11 sides? (*Hendecasyllabic* means "a word with 11 syllables.")

Let students know that they can continue to add words to the chart over the next few days, or however long students' interest continues.

CLASS   GROUPS

ACTIVITY

②*LogoPaths* Activity: Introducing 600 Steps (optional)

In this activity, students use *Free Explore* in the *LogoPaths* software to draw rectangles with perimeters of 600 turtle steps. As with *Missing Measures,* students may enter commands of any amount, not just multiples of 10 as was the case in the Grade 3 activities, *Get the Toys* and *Feed the Turtle,* where students were limited to moves of ten turtle steps. While the software allows them to enter commands to make angles of any size, they will need to make right and left turns of 90 degrees in order to create rectangles.

In Grade 3 you learned an activity called *200 Steps,* in which you used the *LogoPaths* software to create as many rectangles as you could with perimeters of 200 turtle steps. Some of you also made rectangles with perimeters of 400 and 500 steps. To do so, you had to use what you know about rectangles to think about what the lengths of the sides could be and what size turns the turtle needed to make. You could use any number you wanted for the length of the sides, not only multiples of ten.

Explain to the students that they are going to do the same activity this year, but with longer perimeters, of 600, 800, or 1,000 steps.

Open *Free Explore* in the *LogoPaths* software. Have students suggest commands to draw the sides and angles needed to create one or two rectangles with perimeters of 600 steps. Ask questions to help them look for strategies in the numbers they choose, explain their thinking, and predict what the resulting rectangle will look like (i.e., Will it be a square? Will it be tall and thin? and so on).

[Marisol] said to use forward 150 for the length of the first side. What does that tell you about how long the other sides will have to be to create a perimeter of 600 steps? What will the rectangle look like?

Students might say:

"I was thinking that there has to be another side that's 150 because the opposite sides of rectangles are the same. So that would make 300 steps so far. That means that the other two sides would have to equal 300 steps together since the perimeter is 600 steps."

"If the other two sides have to equal 300 steps together, then the shape will be a square. All four sides will be 150 steps."

[Luke] suggested using forward 270 for the length of the first side. How long will the other sides be? What will this rectangle look like?

Students might say:

"It's the same as with the other rectangle. There has to be another side that's 270 steps, so that would use up 540 steps. That leaves 60 steps for the other two sides or 30 steps each. The rectangle would be really long and skinny."

"I would do it a different way. I think about a long side and a short side and know they have to add together to equal half of the perimeter. 270 steps is the long side, so the short side has to be 30 steps to get to 300. Then, there's another 270 and another 30."

Solicit further suggestions from the students to complete one or two rectangles. At the end of the procedure, use the **HT** (hide turtle) command to check whether or not the rectangle is complete. You can use **ST** (show turtle) to make the turtle visible again. Then use the Label Lengths tool to label the length of each line segment and let students know they will do the same when they make their own rectangles. Students should also use the Teach Tool to name and save the procedure for each rectangle they create.

MATH WORKSHOP

3 Working with Polygons

50 MIN

Students work on three activities in this Math Workshop, which will continue in the next session. They play *Guess My Rule* with Shape Cards, and they continue to make polygons with different numbers of sides by combining Power Polygons. They may also work with the *LogoPaths* software on the computer. Students should all play at least a few rounds of *Guess My Rule,* and then choose between the other two activities.

Spend a few minutes at the beginning of Math Workshop introducing students to the Shape Cards (M19–M20), which they will use to play several versions of *Guess My Rule* over the next couple of sessions.

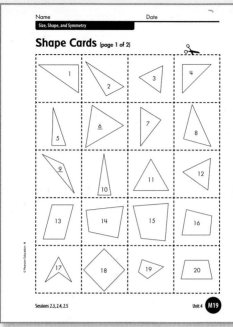

▲ Resource Masters, M19; T47

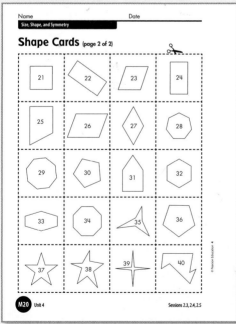

▲ Resource Masters, M20; T48

① Shape Cards In order to keep track of individual sets, suggest that students make an identifying mark, like a colored squiggle, on the back of each of the cards in the set they are working with. Or, you may do this yourself when you prepare the Shape Card sets. Shape Cards may be stored in envelopes.

Professional Development

② Teacher Note: Beyond Vocabulary, p. 154

Name _____ Date _____

Size, Shape, and Symmetry

Sorting Polygons

Record at least 3 rules that you and your partner made for polygons when you played *Guess My Rule*. For each rule, write the numbers of the Shape Cards that fit the rule, and the numbers of 2 or 3 Shape Cards that did not fit the rule. (You may record more than 3 rules, or use this same sheet for another game.)

Rule	Polygons That Fit the Rule	Polygons That Do Not Fit the Rule

22 Unit 4   Sessions 2.3, 2.5

© Pearson Education 4

▲ **Student Activity Book, p. 22**

Students playing Guess My Rule *with Shape Cards.*

③A *Guess My Rule* with Shape Cards

PAIRS

Distribute the sets of Shape Cards to pairs of students. **①** Remind them to choose two cards that fit their rule, and one that does not, as they begin each round. Partners take turns being the one who thinks up a rule.

After students have played several rounds, they choose three or four rules from their game to record on *Student Activity Book* page 22. They write the letters of polygons that fit each rule, and several examples of polygons that did not fit. **②**

As you watch students playing *Guess My Rule,* notice what attributes of polygons they are paying attention to as they choose their rules. This will give you an opportunity to see what students understand about the properties of polygons at this point. Here are some examples of rules you might see students choosing:

Has _____ sides

Has at least one right angle

Has all sides the same

Has a long skinny angle

Has an angle that's larger than a right angle

Has all sides different

Has two sides that are the same

Has opposite sides that are like railroad tracks (parallel)

Has a side that's bent in (concave)

ONGOING ASSESSMENT: Observing Students at Work

Students sort polygons according to various attributes, including number of sides, length of sides, and size of angles.

- **What attributes do students pay attention to as they make their rules?** Do these include side length and angle size? Do students consider orientation an attribute (i.e., they consider a triangle that sits on its base a different shape from a triangle that has no horizontal sides)?

- **What geometric terms do students use to articulate their rules?** Do they include the names for polygons, terms such as *side*, *angle*, and *vertex*, or descriptions such as *right angle*, *parallel sides*, or *concave shape?*

3B Making Polygons

INDIVIDUALS

Students either complete their work on *Student Activity Book* pages 18–19 from Session 2.2, or go on to making polygons with more than six sides on *Student Activity Book* pages 23–24.

ONGOING ASSESSMENT: Observing Students at Work

Students construct polygons of various shapes, with different numbers of sides.

- **Can students combine two or more polygons to make a new shape that is a closed figure?**

- **Do students trace around the outside edge of the polygonal shapes and correctly count the number of sides?**

DIFFERENTIATION: Supporting the Range of Learners

Extension As students work on making polygons with many sides, challenge some students to try to make a series of related shapes. For example:

- How can you start with a hexagon (six sides), and change it so that there are seven sides? Can you then make it eight sides, nine sides, etc.?

This variation offers students the opportunity to make their polygons more strategically.

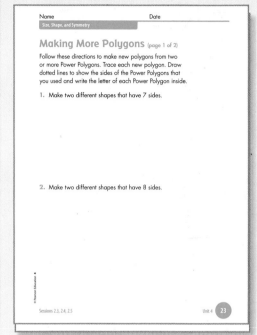

▲ Student Activity Book, pp. 23–24

▲ Resource Masters, M4

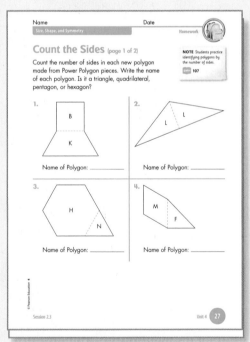

▲ **Student Activity Book, pp. 25–26**

▲ **Student Activity Book, pp. 27–28**

③C *LogoPaths* Activity: *600 Steps* (optional) INDIVIDUALS PAIRS

Students work alone or with partners on this *LogoPaths* activity in which they use turtle commands to draw different rectangles with perimeters of 600 steps. They build as many rectangles as they can with this perimeter. They choose four of the rectangles to sketch and label on *LogoPaths: 600 Steps, Rectangles* (M4). Observe your students working on *LogoPaths* to see whether they can use the commands fluently to move and turn the turtle.

A teacher observes as students work on LogoPaths.

ONGOING ASSESSMENT: Observing Students at Work

Students use their understanding of perimeter and the structure of rectangles to create different rectangles with perimeters of 600 steps.

- **Do they use right and left turns consistently and correctly even when the turtle is not facing straight up?** Do they demonstrate understanding that in order to make rectangles they must use turns of 90 degrees?

- **Do students demonstrate knowledge that parallel sides of rectangles must be equal?**

- **Are they able to create multiple rectangles with perimeters of 600 steps?** Do they do so by trial and error or have they figured out a strategy to find new rectangles with the same perimeter?

- **Do they look for a pair of numbers for the first two sides that add to one half the perimeter (e.g., 250 and 50 when the perimeter is 600) and use that pair again for the length of the third and fourth sides?**

- **Do they recognize that they can start with a set of dimensions for a rectangle with a perimeter of 600, subtract the same number of steps from one pair of parallel sides, and then add them to the other pair of parallel sides to create a new rectangle with a perimeter of 600?** For example, a rectangle with two sides 250 steps long and two sides 50 steps long can be changed to a rectangle with pairs of sides 225 (250 − 25) and 75 (50 + 25) steps long.

DIFFERENTIATION: Supporting the Range of Learners

Extension Students moving easily through this activity are probably using a strategy to help them create new rectangles. Help them think about whether their strategy would work with any rectangle. ❸ Ask questions like the following:

- I see you made a rectangle with sides 170, 130, 170, and 130 steps long. Can you start with that rectangle and make another one that would also have a perimeter of 600 steps?

- Could you use that strategy again to turn your new rectangle into another one that works? Do you think your strategy would work with any rectangle?

SESSION FOLLOW-UP
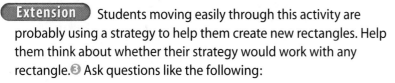

④ Daily Practice and Homework

 Daily Practice: For ongoing review, have students complete *Student Activity Book* pages 25–26.

 Homework: On *Student Activity Book* pages 27–28 students name given polygons according to the number of sides.

 Student Math Handbook: Students and families may use *Student Math Handbook* page 107 for reference and review. See pages 170–174 in the back of this unit.

Technology Note

❸ **Variable Inputs for Rectangles** As students enter commands to draw rectangles, they are likely to notice that each new rectangle procedure they **"Teach"** the turtle differs from previous rectangle procedures only in the specific lengths of the sides. Consider teaching these students how to write a procedure for rectangles. Since all rectangles have four 90 degree angles, and two sets of opposite equal sides, it is the lengths of the sides that are the variables.

Step 1: *Define a new procedure*
Begin a new procedure by typing "to" and the procedure name on a new line in the Teach window.
For example, **to RECTANGLE**

Step 2: *Define the variables*
Just after the procedure name on the line, name the variables preceded by colons.
For example, **:SIDE1 :SIDE2** etc.
(The colon is pronounced "dots.")

Step 3: *Define the procedure*
A procedure for a rectangle can be defined with four inputs as shown below:

```
to RECTANGLE :SIDE1 :SIDE2
FD :SIDE1 RT 90 FD :SIDE2 RT 90
FD :SIDE1 RT 90 FD :SIDE2 RT 90
end
```

The turtle moves forward according to the steps indicated in the first input, turns right 90 degrees, then moves forward according to the steps indicated in the second input, turns right 90 degrees, and then does those steps over again.

Step 4: *Use the procedure to draw rectangles*
To use this procedure, type **RECTANGLE** and the side lengths in the **Command Center**. For example, **RECTANGLE 100 200** Entering these commands will result in a rectangle 100 turtle steps tall and 200 turtle steps wide. Students can input different side lengths to draw different rectangles.

Sorting Quadrilaterals

Math Focus Points

◆ Developing vocabulary to describe attributes and properties of quadrilaterals

◆ Combining polygons to make new polygons

Vocabulary

quadrilateral

Today's Plan		Materials
ACTIVITY **①** Introducing *Guess My Rule* with Quadrilaterals	10 MIN CLASS	• M19–M20 (from Session 2.3)
MATH WORKSHOP **②** Working with Polygons ② Ⓐ *Guess My Rule* with Quadrilaterals ② Ⓑ Making Polygons ② Ⓒ *LogoPaths* Activity: *600 Steps*	35 MIN	Ⓐ • *Student Activity Book,* p. 29 • M19–M20 (from Session 2.3) Ⓑ • *Student Activity Book,* pp. 18–19; pp. 23–24; pp. 30–32 • Power Polygons Ⓒ • M4* • Computers with *LogoPaths* software installed*
DISCUSSION **③** All Quadrilaterals . . . Some Quadrilaterals	15 MIN CLASS	• Chart: "All Quadrilaterals . . . Some Quadrilaterals . . ."*
SESSION FOLLOW-UP **④** Daily Practice		• *Student Activity Book,* p. 33 • *Student Math Handbook,* pp. 108–110

*See *Materials to Prepare,* p. 53.

Ten-Minute Math

Quick Images: 2-D Show Images 7 and 8 (one at a time) from *Quick Images: 2-D* (T43) and follow the procedure for the basic routine. For each image, students discuss how they drew their figures, including any revisions they made after each viewing.

Ask students:

• How did you remember the parts of the image?

• What did you notice about the relationship of the parts of the image?

• What helped you remember the whole image, so you could draw your design?

ACTIVITY

① Introducing *Guess My Rule* with Quadrilaterals

Begin this session by asking students to find all the quadrilaterals in their Shape Cards set. The quadrilaterals are the shapes 13 through 27; however, rather than telling students which cards are the quadrilaterals, have them work with a partner to separate the cards from the rest of the set. This will give you an opportunity to see what students understand about the properties of quadrilaterals at this point.

Who remembers what a quadrilateral is? How many sides does a quadrilateral have?

Students should know, from their work in earlier grades as well as from the homework about names for polygons, that a quadrilateral is a four-sided shape. As they separate these from the rest of the shapes in their Shape Cards sets, notice whether they include *all* four-sided shapes as quadrilaterals. If students have excluded some of the quadrilaterals because of orientation (such as shapes 18, 22, or 27), ask them whether it might change their thinking if they turn the cards so that the shapes look more familiar to them.

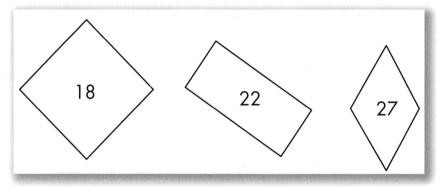

If students have excluded some shapes because of the size of the angles (for example, shapes 17 and 19 may look "triangle-like" to some students), ask them to count the sides and consider how many sides a shape has to have to be a quadrilateral.

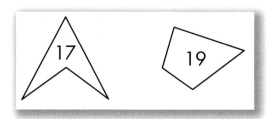

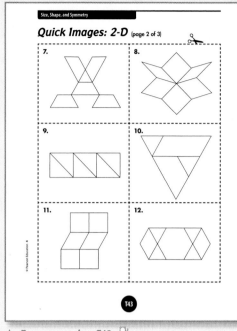

▲ Transparencies, T43

▲ Student Activity Book, p. 29

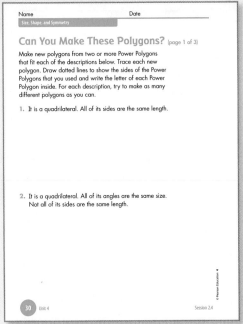

Name _____ **Date** _____

Size, Shape, and Symmetry

Can You Make These Polygons? (page 1 of 3)

Make new polygons from two or more Power Polygons that fit each of the descriptions below. Trace each new polygon. Draw dotted lines to show the sides of the Power Polygons that you used and write the letter of each Power Polygon inside. For each description, try to make as many different polygons as you can.

1. It is a quadrilateral. All of its sides are the same length.

2. It is a quadrilateral. All of its angles are the same size. Not all of its sides are the same length.

30   Unit 4   Session 2.4

▲ **Student Activity Book, p. 30**

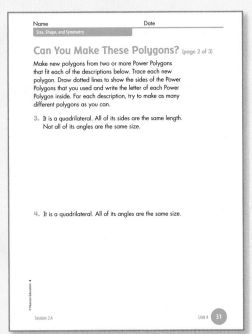

Name _____ **Date** _____

Size, Shape, and Symmetry

Can You Make These Polygons? (page 2 of 3)

Make new polygons from two or more Power Polygons that fit each of the descriptions below. Trace each new polygon. Draw dotted lines to show the sides of the Power Polygons that you used and write the letter of each Power Polygon inside. For each description, try to make as many different polygons as you can.

3. It is a quadrilateral. All of its sides are the same length. Not all of its angles are the same size.

4. It is a quadrilateral. All of its angles are the same size.

Session 2.4   Unit 4   31

▲ **Student Activity Book, p. 31**

Once students have separated the quadrilateral Shape Cards, let them know that they will be playing a version of *Guess My Rule* with just these cards in Math Workshop today.

When you're playing *Guess My Rule* with Quadrilaterals, think about what's true about all quadrilaterals, and what's true about only some of them. In other words, what are the attributes that make some quadrilaterals different from others, even though they are all quadrilaterals? We'll come back and talk about this at the end of the session.

MATH WORKSHOP

② Working with Polygons

35 MIN

Students continue working on the Math Workshop activities from the last session. All students should play at least a few rounds of *Guess My Rule* with Quadrilaterals before the discussion at the end of the session.

②A *Guess My Rule* with Quadrilaterals

PAIRS

Students play this version of *Guess My Rule* the same way that they played *Guess My Rule* with Shape Cards, focusing only on quadrilaterals. They record their thinking about what is true for all quadrilaterals and what is true for only some quadrilaterals on *Student Activity Book* page 29.

ONGOING ASSESSMENT: Observing Students at Work

Students sort quadrilaterals according to various attributes, including length of sides and size of angles.

- **Do the attributes that students pay attention to as they make their rules include both side length and angle size?** Do students consider orientation an attribute (i.e., they consider a square that sits on one vertex a different shape from a square that sits on one side)?

- **What geometric terms do students use to articulate their rules?** Do they include the names for some quadrilaterals (square, rectangle, rhombus, trapezoid, parallelogram), terms such as *side, angle,* and *vertex,* or descriptions such as *right angle, parallel sides,* or *concave shape?*

2B Making Polygons

INDIVIDUALS

Students who have completed *Student Activity Book* pages 18–19 and *Student Activity Book* pages 23–24 can go on to *Student Activity Book* pages 30–32. On these pages, students use the Power Polygons to make polygons that fit given rules. It is possible that not all students will get to this activity in this or the next Math Workshop. If that is the case, leave the Power Polygons available so that students can continue working with them during free time outside of math class, or when they have completed their work in later sessions in this unit.

ONGOING ASSESSMENT: Observing Students at Work

Students construct polygons that fit given descriptions.

- **Can students combine two or more polygons to make a new shape that fits the given description?**

2C *LogoPaths* Activity: *600 Steps*

PAIRS   INDIVIDUALS

For complete details about this activity, see Session 2.3, pages 67–69. ❶

---

3 DISCUSSION

All Quadrilaterals . . . Some Quadrilaterals

15 MIN   CLASS

Math Focus Points for Discussion

◆ Developing vocabulary to describe attributes and properties of quadrilaterals

Begin the discussion by asking for some of the rules that students used for *Guess My Rule* with Quadrilaterals. As students give their rules, write several of them on the board or overhead, using the students' language and introducing geometric vocabulary at the same time. For example:

[Derek], you and [Bill] had a rule in your game for quadrilaterals with wide angles. We also call these angles, when they're bigger than a 90-degree or right angle, *obtuse angles.* Another way to say your rule might be "quadrilaterals with obtuse angles." ❷

Within the activity book image:

Name   Date

Size, Shape, and Symmetry

Can You Make These Polygons? (page 3 of 3)

Make new polygons from two or more Power
Polygons that fit each of the descriptions below.
Trace each new polygon. Draw dotted lines to show
the sides of the Power Polygons that you used and
write the letter of each Power Polygon inside. For
each description, try to make as many different
polygons as you can.

5. It is a triangle. All of its sides are the same length.

6. It is a triangle. All of its angles are different sizes.

32 Unit 4   Session 2.4

Show the chart labeled "All Quadrilaterals . . . " and "Some Quadrilaterals . . . "

You have noticed that all quadrilaterals have four sides. (Record this under "All Quadrilaterals . . . ") What else do all quadrilaterals have?

Add students' suggestions to the chart. It is important that students identify quadrilaterals as being a four-sided polygon or closed shape. They may also add "have four angles" and "have four vertices" to this list.

Students share suggestions of rules for quadrilaterals.

You also noticed that there are some differences among quadrilaterals. Think about the ways you sorted the quadrilaterals for *Guess My Rule.* What are some ways we can complete this statement: "Some quadrilaterals . . . "?

List the different attributes students mention such as "Some quadrilaterals have all 90-degree angles," or "Some quadrilaterals have two pairs of parallel sides." You can use this as another opportunity to offer the formal geometric terms for the idea they are expressing.

One possible chart might look like this:

All quadrilaterals . . .	Some quadrilaterals . . .
have 4 lines, segments, or sides	have a right (or 90°) angle or turn (are perpendicular)
have no rounded corners, no crossing lines (are polygons)	have parallel lines (going in the same direction, equidistant from each other)
have angles that add up to 360°	have all equal sides (square or rhombus)
can have different shapes and sizes (don't have to be perfect)	have 2 sides parallel and other 2 sides parallel (parallelogram)
have 4 angles, corners, points, or vertices	have no sides the same (nonregular)
	have acute angles and obtuse angles

Post the chart where students can refer to it in the next session when they discuss squares and rectangles specifically.

SESSION FOLLOW-UP

4 Daily Practice

 Daily Practice: For reinforcement of this unit's content, have students complete *Student Activity Book* page 33.

 Student Math Handbook: Students and families may use *Student Math Handbook* pages 108–110 for reference and review. See pages 170–174 in the back of this unit.

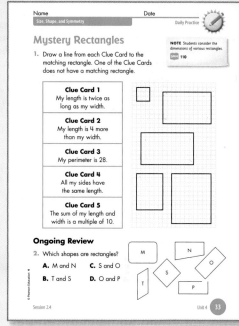

▲ **Student Activity Book, p. 33**

Assessment: What Is a Quadrilateral?

Math Focus Points

◆ Understanding the relationship between squares and rectangles

◆ Developing vocabulary to describe attributes and properties of quadrilaterals

Vocabulary

square
rectangle

Today's Plan			Materials
DISCUSSION ① **Is It a Square or a Rectangle?**	🕐 20 MIN	👥 PAIRS	• Power Polygons, Shapes A and C
ASSESSMENT ACTIVITY ② **What Is a Quadrilateral?**	✓ 🕐 20 MIN	👤 INDIVIDUALS	• M21*
MATH WORKSHOP ③ **Working with Polygons** ③A *Guess My Rule* (with Power Polygons or Shape Cards) ③B **Making Polygons** ③C *LogoPaths* Activity: *600 Steps* or *800 Steps* (optional)	🕐 20 MIN		③A • Student Activity Book, p. 22 • M19, M20 (from Session 2.3) • Scissors; envelopes; Power Polygons ③B • *Student Activity Book*, pp. 18–19; pp. 23–24 • Power Polygons; pie plates or plastic containers (optional) ③C • M4 (optional)*; M5; (optional)* • Computers with *LogoPaths* software installed*
SESSION FOLLOW-UP ④ **Daily Practice and Homework**			• *Student Activity Book*, pp. 34–36 • *Student Math Handbook*, pp. 108–109

*See *Materials to Prepare*, p. 53.

Ten-Minute Math

Quick Images: 2-D Show Images 9 and 10 (one at a time) from *Quick Images 2-D* (T43) and follow the procedure for the basic routine. For each image, students discuss how they drew their figures, including any revisions they made after each viewing. Ask students: How did you remember the parts of the image? What did you notice about the relationship of the parts of the image? What helped you remember the whole image so that you could draw your design?

① Is It a Square or a Rectangle?

20 MIN   PAIRS

Professional Development

① **Teacher Note:** Classification of Quadrilaterals, p. 155

Math Focus Points for Discussion

◆ Understanding the relationship between squares and rectangles

Begin the session by reviewing with students the definition of a quadrilateral that they came up with in the last session.

Yesterday we said that all quadrilaterals have to have four sides and four angles. We also noticed that quadrilaterals can look different from one another, depending on the size of the angles or the lengths of the sides. Here are some questions for you to think about.

Hold up the yellow square Power Polygon (piece A), and ask a series of questions about how to classify this shape.

- *Is this shape a polygon? How do you know?*

- *Is it a quadrilateral? How do you know?*

- *So this shape is both a polygon and a quadrilateral. Could it also be a rectangle? Talk about this with your partner for a minute and then we'll see what you think.*①

Give students a few minutes to discuss this in pairs. They may use Power Polygon shapes A and C (a blue rectangle) to compare the two. It is likely that students may have very different opinions. As you listen in, make note of which students are basing their arguments on the properties of the two shapes, squares and rectangles, rather than solely on what they look like. Plan to call on these students to share their thinking. Call the class back together.

I heard some of you say that this shape is just a square, *because it looks like a square. What does a shape have to have to be a square?*

Students should be able to say that a square has four sides that are all the same length. Some students may add that a square has four right angles, and that the sides are parallel. List these properties on the board as students mention them.

Some of you thought that you could also call it a rectangle, *so it could be both. [Cheyenne] and [Lucy], why did you think it could also be a rectangle?*

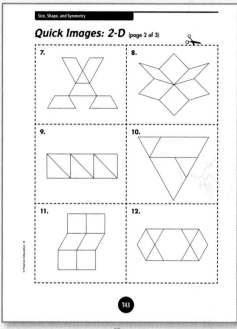

Size, Shape, and Symmetry

Quick Images: 2-D (page 2 of 3)

▲ Transparencies, T43

Name _____ Date _____

Size, Shape, and Symmetry

Assessment: What Is a Quadrilateral?

Using the Power Polygons, choose one shape that is a quadrilateral and one shape that is not a quadrilateral. Draw these in the spaces below and explain why each is or is not a quadrilateral.

Quadrilateral:	Not a Quadrilateral:
This shape is a quadrilateral because:	This shape is not a quadrilateral because:

Pretend you are talking on the telephone to someone who is not sure what a quadrilateral is. What would you say to help them draw a quadrilateral? Write your description on the back of this sheet.

Session 2.5   Unit 4 **M21**

▲ **Resource Masters, M21** PORTFOLIO

Students might say:

"The only thing that's different between a square and a rectangle is that a square has to have all sides the same, and a rectangle doesn't. But a rectangle could have all sides the same, like some triangles do. It would be like an equilateral rectangle! And then it's a square."

As students argue this idea, help them focus their definitions of squares and rectangles by continuing to refer to their shared properties. Although it is mathematically true that squares are a special kind of rectangle (since the definition of rectangle refers to the number and size of the angles and not to the length of the sides), not all students will be convinced of this by the end of this discussion.❷

ASSESSMENT ACTIVITY

2 What Is a Quadrilateral?

20 MIN INDIVIDUALS

On Assessment: What Is a Quadrilateral? (M21), students choose two shapes from the Power Polygon set, one that is and one that is not a quadrilateral, and explain their choice. They write a description of a quadrilateral.❸ This assessment addresses Benchmark 2: Identify quadrilaterals as any four-sided closed figure.

ONGOING ASSESSMENT: Observing Students at Work

Students describe the properties of quadrilaterals.

- **Do students know that a quadrilateral is a four-sided figure?** Do they choose any quadrilaterals other than squares and rectangles?

- **Do students describe quadrilaterals only by the number of sides and angles?** Or do they include properties that describe only certain quadrilaterals, such as "four equal sides"?

MATH WORKSHOP

20 MIN

③ Working with Polygons

After students have completed and turned in the assessment, they choose from the Math Workshop activities of the last two sessions.

PAIRS

③A *Guess My Rule* (with Power Polygons or Shape Cards)

For complete details about this activity, see Sessions 2.1, pages 58–59, and 2.3, page 70. Students may play any of the versions of the game they have played so far, using either the Shape Cards or the Power Polygons.

INDIVIDUALS

③B Making Polygons

For complete details about this activity, see Session 2.2, pages 63–64.

PAIRS   INDIVIDUALS

③C *LogoPaths* Activity: *600 Steps* or *800 Steps* (optional)

For complete details about this activity, see Session 2.3, pages 67–69.

DIFFERENTIATION: Supporting the Range of Learners

Extension Students who completed the *600 Steps* activity in the previous Math Workshops can move on to *800 Steps*, following the same procedure as the *600 Steps* activity. They sketch at least four of the rectangles with perimeters of 800 and label the sides on *LogoPaths: 800 Steps, Rectangles* (M5).

SESSION FOLLOW-UP

④ Daily Practice and Homework

Daily Practice: For ongoing review, have students complete *Student Activity Book* page 34.

Homework: On *Student Activity Book* pages 35–36, students sort quadrilaterals by identifying right angles, parallel sides, and equal side lengths. They also draw quadrilaterals that meet given criteria.

Student Math Handbook: Students and families may use *Student Math Handbook* pages 108–109 for reference and review. See pages 170–174 in the back of this unit.

Name _____ **Date** _____
Size, Shape, and Symmetry
Daily Practice

Today's Number:
Broken Calculator

NOTE Students practice building flexibility with all operations (addition, subtraction, multiplication, and division).

Find five solutions to each of these problems.

1. I want to make 36 using my calculator, but the 3 key and the 6 key are broken. How can I use my calculator to do this task?

2. I want to make 200 using my calculator, but the 0 key and the + key are broken. How can I use my calculator to do this task?

3. I want to make 64 using my calculator, but the 6 key and the 4 key are broken. How can I use my calculator to do this task?

4. I want to make 55 using my calculator, but the 5 key, the + key, and the − key are broken. How can I use my calculator to do this task?

34 Unit 4   Session 2.5

▲ **Student Activity Book, p. 34**

Name _____ **Date** _____
Size, Shape, and Symmetry
Homework

Sorting Quadrilaterals (page 1 of 2)

NOTE Students practice identifying properties in quadrilaterals.
SMH 108–109

Write the numbers of all the quadrilaterals that belong in each category.

1. Which quadrilaterals have 4 right angles?
_____

2. Which quadrilaterals have 2 pairs of parallel sides?
_____

3. Which quadrilaterals have 4 sides of equal length?
_____

Session 2.5   Unit 4 **35**

▲ **Student Activity Book, pp. 35–36**

Mathematical Emphasis

Features of Shapes Describing and measuring angles

Math Focus Points

◆ Identifying a right angle as 90 degrees

◆ Measuring acute angles by relating them to 90 degrees

◆ Using known angles to find the measure of other angles

Measuring Angles

	Student Activity Book	Student Math Handbook	Professional Development: Read Ahead of Time	
SESSION 3.1　　　p. 88				
Making Right Angles Students use Power Polygons to make right angles. They compare the measure of acute angles to right angles and use what they know about 90 degrees to determine the measure of these angles.	37–38	111–113		
SESSION 3.2　　　p. 94				
More or Less Than 90 Degrees? Students continue to measure angles with Power Polygons. They build angles of 60, 120, and 150 degrees.	39–45	111–113	• **Dialogue Box:** Building Angles, p. 167	
SESSION 3.3　　　p. 102				
Assessment: Building Angles Students are assessed on their ability to identify angles of various measures as they continue to measure and build angles with Power Polygons. They discuss their strategies for constructing both acute and obtuse angles.	39–43, 47–49	111–113		

Materials to Gather	Materials to Prepare
• **Power Polygons** (handful per 3–4 students and 1 set for each shape for the class)	
• **Power Polygons** (handful per 3–4 students and 1 set for each shape for the class) • **Two rulers**	• **M6,** *LogoPaths: 600 Steps, Other Polygons* Make copies. (1 per student; optional) • **Computers with** *LogoPaths* **software installed** (optional)
• **Power Polygons** (handful per 3–4 students and 1 set for each shape for the class)	• **M22, Assessment Checklist: Building Angles** ☑ Make copies. (1 per 8 students) • **M7,** *LogoPaths: 800 Steps, Other Polygons* Make copies. (1 per student; optional) • **Computers with** *LogoPaths* **software installed** (optional)

☑ Checklist Available

Making Right Angles

Math Focus Points

- Identifying a right angle as 90 degrees
- Measuring acute angles by relating them to 90 degrees

Vocabulary

angle	right angle
degree	equilateral triangle

Today's Plan		Materials
1 ACTIVITY **Introducing Making Right Angles**	10 MIN CLASS	• Power Polygons
2 ACTIVITY **Making Right Angles**	30 MIN PAIRS	• *Student Activity Book*, p. 37 • Power Polygons
3 DISCUSSION **How Many Degrees?**	20 MIN CLASS	• Power Polygons
4 SESSION FOLLOW-UP **Daily Practice**		• *Student Activity Book*, p. 38 • *Student Math Handbook*, pp. 111–113

Ten-Minute Math

Today's Number: Broken Calculator Students create five expressions that equal 1,450. They must use both addition and subtraction in their expressions. The 4 and 5 keys are broken. Have two or three students share their equations and explain how they know that the answer is correct. (Examples: $3,000 - 1,800 + 220 + 30 = 1,450$ or $1,000 + 610 - 160 = 1,450$)

ACTIVITY

1 Introducing Making Right Angles

10 MIN   CLASS

Begin the session by placing Power Polygon shape A (yellow square) on the overhead. Tell students that for the next few sessions, they are going to be examining the angles in polygons.

Invite one or two students to come up and identify the four angles in the square. Ask them what they know about the angles in the polygon.

Students are likely to describe the angles in the square in three different ways: they are right angles, they are 90 degrees, or they are like the corner of a sheet of paper. Reinforce for students that the angles in the square are called right angles and have a measurement of 90 degrees.

In our last few sessions, you were placing the Power Polygons next to each other to see what kinds of new polygons you could make. Today we are going to do something similar, but instead of focusing on the shape, we are going to be paying attention to the angles. Take a look at your Power Polygon pieces, and see whether you can find two that fit together to make a right angle.

Give students a minute to work on this. Suggest that students use a corner of a sheet of paper or the angles in the large square polygon piece (A) as a reference for the right angle.

Once most students have found a way to make a right angle, call the class together to share a couple of examples. Some combinations will form a familiar polygon. Some combinations (see the example from polygons N and L) will not form a familiar shape. If possible, use examples from student work to illustrate both of these situations.

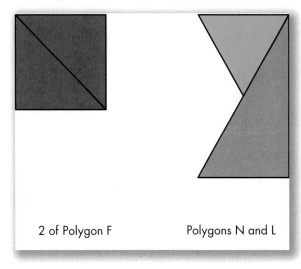

2 of Polygon F   Polygons N and L

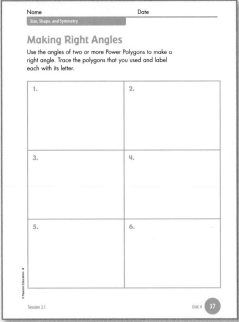

▲ **Student Activity Book, p. 37**

I see several examples of two polygons that fit together to make a 90-degree angle. Each of these smaller angles is less than 90 degrees. Later on we will find the measurements of each of these smaller angles as well as some that are bigger than 90 degrees.

30 MIN PAIRS

ACTIVITY

2 Making Right Angles

Students continue to work on making right angles, and record their work on *Student Activity Book* page 37.

Work with a partner to find more ways to make a 90-degree angle using some of the smaller angles of the Power Polygons. See whether you can find an example of *more* than two angles that will fit into the 90-degree angle.

As you observe students working on making right angles, help them begin to use numerical reasoning to determine the degree measures of the angles by asking questions such as:

I see you have arranged three of the same angles to make that right angle, or 90-degree angle. What does that tell you about the size of each angle?

If students offer such arguments on their own, ask them to justify their reasoning.

You say that these two make 90 degrees and so each of them is 45 degrees. How do you know that they are the same size?

While there are a limited number of combinations of the Power Polygon angles that equal 90 degrees [45 + 45; 30 + 60; 30 + 30 + 30], students will discover that several polygons have angles that are the same size. (For example, the angles in shape I and N and two of the angles in G are all the same size, 60 degrees.)

*A student uses Power Polygons to create
a right angle.*

ONGOING ASSESSMENT: Observing Students at Work

Students use Power Polygon shapes to find combinations of angles that equal 90 degrees.

- **Do students easily recognize the shape of a right angle?** Do they use the corner of a square such as shape A or the corner of their paper as a tool for measuring a right angle?

- **Can students find combinations of angles that fit into a 90-degree angle exactly?** Do they notice angles that are the same size? For example, "I found that an angle from G and L fit together to make 90 degrees, so I know that an angle from G and J will fit because J and L have an equal angle."

DIFFERENTIATION: Supporting the Range of Learners

Extension   If some students finish quickly, ask them to find several angles that are equal and determine the measurements. For example, ask,

- What shapes have an angle equal to the angles in the equilateral triangle and what is the measure of that angle?

DISCUSSION

3 How Many Degrees?

Math Focus Points for Discussion

◆ Measuring acute angles by relating them to 90 degrees

Once students have made several combinations of angles that equal 90 degrees, bring them together to consider the measure of the smaller angles. First focus on the 45-degree and 30-degree angles.

Since we already know that the right angle is 90 degrees, let's see how we can use that to help us think about the measure of these smaller angles. I noticed that some of you found that you can put two of the small angles from shape E together to make 90 degrees. [Show two shape E's covering A on the overhead.] Do you know the measure of these small angles in shape E?

Teachers can use Power Polygons to demonstrate how a 90° angle can be made from two smaller equal-sized angles.

Students might say:

"Two of these angles fit into the 90-degree angle exactly, so each one has to be 45 degrees."

I also noticed that some of you used *three* angles to equal 90 degrees. [Show three of the 30-degree angles in shape O filling up the 90-degree angle in shape A.] Can you figure out the measure of these angles?

Three Power Polygons with 30° angles can be used to match the 90° angle of a larger Power Polygon.

Students might say:

"All of these small angles are the same size so they each have to be 30 to add up to 90 degrees."

Now we know the measure of three angles in these Power Polygon shapes. 90, 60, and 30 degrees.

Explain to students that in the next session, they will go on to find the measure of other angles using the Power Polygons.

SESSION FOLLOW-UP

4 Daily Practice

 Daily Practice: For reinforcement of this unit's content, have students complete *Student Activity Book* page 38.

 Student Math Handbook: Students and families may use *Student Math Handbook* pages 111–113 for reference and review. See pages 170–174 in the back of this unit.

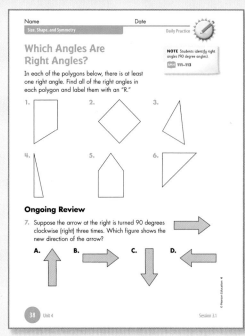

Name _____ Date _____

Size, Shape, and Symmetry   Daily Practice

Which Angles Are Right Angles?

NOTE Students identify right angles (90 degree angles).

111–113

In each of the polygons below, there is at least one right angle. Find all of the right angles in each polygon and label them with an "R."

1.   2.   3.

4.   5.   6.

Ongoing Review

7. Suppose the arrow at the right is turned 90 degrees clockwise (right) three times. Which figure shows the new direction of the arrow?

A.   B.   C.   D.

38 Unit 4   Session 3.1

▲ **Student Activity Book, p. 38**

More or Less Than 90 Degrees?

Math Focus Points

◆ Measuring acute angles by relating them to 90 degrees

◆ Using known angles to find the measure of other angles

Vocabulary

acute
obtuse

Today's Plan		Materials
ACTIVITY ① **Introducing Building Angles** 15 MIN CLASS		• Power Polygons
MATH WORKSHOP ② **Measuring and Building Angles** 30 MIN ② **How Many Degrees?** ② **Building Angles** ② *LogoPaths* Activity: *600 Steps, Other Polygons* (optional)		**2A** • *Student Activity Book*, pp. 39–40 • Power Polygons **2B** • *Student Activity Book*, pp. 41–43 • Power Polygons **2C** • M6 (optional)* • Computers with *LogoPaths* software installed*
DISCUSSION ③ **Smallest Angle, Biggest Angle** 15 MIN CLASS		• Two rulers
SESSION FOLLOW-UP ④ **Daily Practice and Homework**		• *Student Activity Book*, pp. 44–45 • *Student Math Handbook*, pp. 111–113

*See *Materials to Prepare*, p. 87.

Ten-Minute Math

Today's Number: Broken Calculator Students create five expressions that equal 882. They must use both addition and subtraction in their expressions. The 2 and 4 keys are broken. Have two or three students share their equations and explain how they know the answer is correct. (Examples: $600 + 300 - 18 = 882$ or $1,000 - 300 + 100 + 88 - 6 = 882$)

ACTIVITY

Introducing Building Angles

Begin the session by placing Power Polygon shape G (green rhombus) on the overhead.

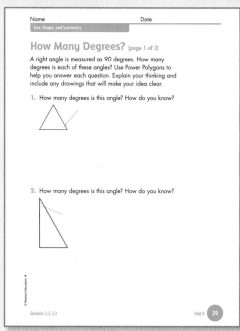

▲ **Student Activity Book, p. 39**

Yesterday we were thinking about how to measure angles that are smaller than a right angle, or less than 90 degrees. Are the angles in this quadrilateral more or less than 90 degrees?

Allow students a minute or two to look carefully at the angles of shape G at their table, comparing each to an angle that they know is 90 degrees. Observe students to see whether they can determine that the two angles in one pair of opposite angles are less than 90 degrees and the angles in the other pair of opposite angles are greater than 90 degrees. Ask one or two students to show what they have found on the overhead. Then introduce new vocabulary for these angles.

Angles that are less than 90 degrees are called *acute* angles [identify the two acute angles in the rhombus]. An acute angle can measure from one degree up to 89 degrees; as long as it's less than 90 degrees, it's an acute angle. The name for angles that are larger than a right angle, or more than 90 degrees, is *obtuse*. We can say that this quadrilateral has two acute angles and two obtuse angles.

Does anyone know how many degrees the acute angles are in this rhombus? Think about the work you did yesterday.

Allow students a few minutes to think about this. Encourage them to compare their answers with a partner and share their thinking. Many students may find that the small angles in shape O are a perfect fit and students may also remember that three of those small angles fit into the right angle, which means that they are each 30 degrees.

Your job today will be to find the measures of some angles and then

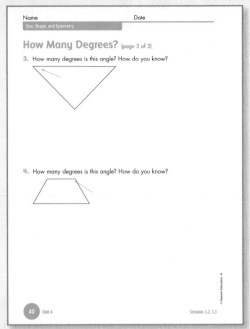

▲ Student Activity Book, p. 40

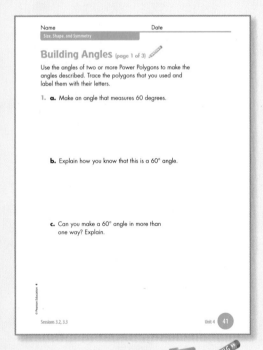

▲ Student Activity Book, p. 41

to build angles that measure 60 degrees, 120 degrees, and 150 degrees. Once you find the measure of one angle on a Power Polygon, see how you can use that to find the measures of other angles.

MATH WORKSHOP

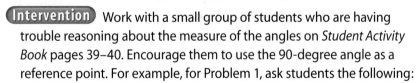

② Measuring and Building Angles

30 MIN

In this Math Workshop, students work on *Student Activity Book* pages 39–43. If you are using the *LogoPaths* software, take a couple of minutes at the start of Math Workshop, or work with small groups of students once Math Workshop begins, to introduce this variation of the *600 Steps* activity. Let students know that their task will no longer be to draw rectangles with perimeters of 600 steps, but to use the *LogoPaths* software to draw polygons with more than four sides with a perimeter of 600 steps.

②A How Many Degrees?

INDIVIDUALS

On *Student Activity Book* pages 39–40, students work individually to find the measure of several angles, by comparing them to 90 degrees.

ONGOING ASSESSMENT: Observing Students at Work

Students determine the measure of angles in relation to 90 degrees.

- **Are students using what they know about 90 degrees to reason about the number of degrees of the angles in the Power Polygon pieces?**

DIFFERENTIATION: Supporting the Range of Learners

Intervention Work with a small group of students who are having trouble reasoning about the measure of the angles on *Student Activity Book* pages 39–40. Encourage them to use the 90-degree angle as a reference point. For example, for Problem 1, ask students the following:

- Is this angle bigger or smaller than the right angle which is 90 degrees?

- Is it more or less than half of the 90-degree angle?

- So it is more than 45 degrees. Are there other angles that would fit in this angle?

- How many of those fit in the 90-degree angle? Does that help you at all?

Extension If students can find the angle measures easily, ask them to find the measures of all the angles in each shape.

2B Building Angles

PAIRS

Students work in pairs on *Student Activity Book* page 41–43. They use the Power Polygon shapes to build 60-, 120-, and 150-degree angles.

As you circulate, ask students how they are using what they have found in one case to help them find the angle sizes in the next polygon. The discussion in the next session will focus on how they built angles of 120 degrees.

ONGOING ASSESSMENT: Observing Students at Work

Students use what they know about the size of angles to build other angles.

- **Can students identify angles that are 30 degrees and 60 degrees?**

- **Can they use these in combination with angles they know to be 90 degrees to build 120-degree and 150-degree angles?**

- **Do students use an angle they have found as a basis for figuring other angle sizes?** For example, once they have determined that an angle is 30 degrees, do they use that angle as a tool for finding other angle measures?

DIFFERENTIATION: Supporting the Range of Learners

Intervention Some students might have difficulty when the two polygons do not form a familiar shape. For example, the smallest angles of shape L and shape O (both 30 degrees) can be combined to make a 60-degree angle, but the entire shape is not a familiar polygon.

Professional Development

❶ Dialogue Box: Building Angles, p. 167

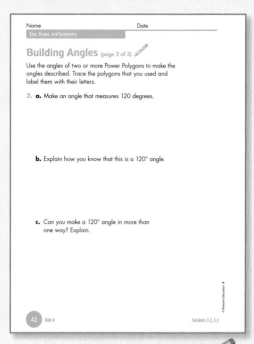

▲ Student Activity Book, p. 42

▲ Student Activity Book, p. 43

LogoPaths: 600 Steps, Other Polygons

Use *LogoPaths Free Explore* to draw two polygons with **more than four sides** that have perimeters of 600 steps. Use **only 90° turns** in your polygons.

1. Sketch the first polygon that you drew in the space below or on the back of this sheet. Label the length of each side.

2. Sketch the second polygon that you drew in the space below or on the back of this sheet. Label the length of each side.

CHALLENGE: Use *LogoPaths Free Explore* to draw an equilateral **triangle** with a perimeter of 600 steps. Use the *Turtle Turner* to help you decide what turning angles you need to enter. Record your commands and sketch the triangle that you drew on the back of this sheet. Label the length of each side.

M6 Unit 4

▲ **Resource Masters, M6**

Math Note

❷ **Relating Turning Angles to Inside Angles of Polygons** As students use the *LogoPaths* software to draw polygons with angles other than 90 degrees, they must pay attention to the relationship between the amount they tell the turtle to turn and the interior angle formed by that turn. For example, to create an interior angle of 60 degrees for an equilateral triangle, the students must turn the turtle 120 degrees. In other words, the turn must be the supplement of the interior angle they wish to form. 120 degrees and 60 degrees are supplementary angles because together they form 180 degrees or a straight line. Students have been doing this all along each time they turned the turtle 90 degrees while drawing squares and rectangles. However, since the interior angle created is also 90 degrees, the relationship was not so readily apparent. Students will have the opportunity to explore these relationships further in Grade 5.

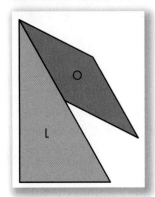

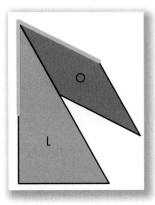

Suggest that students only trace around the angle that they are examining to help them focus on that aspect of the polygon.

- -

❷⒞ LogoPaths Activity: *600 Steps, Other Polygons* (optional)

INDIVIDUALS PAIRS

Students work alone or with partners on this *LogoPaths* activity. Using forward and backward moves and 90-degree turns, they draw polygons with more than four sides that have perimeters of 600 steps. They sketch the polygons and label the lengths of the sides on *LogoPaths: 600 Steps, Other Polygons* (M6).

After completing these two polygons, students are challenged to draw an equilateral triangle with a perimeter of 600 steps. They record the commands they used, sketch the triangle, and label the length of the sides on the paper. Do not expect all fourth graders to be successful with this task, because creating the correct relationship between the length of the sides and the size of the angles is a complex task. However, they will benefit from experimenting with changing the lengths of the sides and the sizes of the turning angles and observing how these changes affect the interior angles formed. ❷

Bring the class together for the discussion when there are about 15 minutes left in the session.

ONGOING ASSESSMENT: Observing Students at Work

Students use their understanding of perimeter and the structure of polygons to create different nonrectangular figures with perimeters of 600 steps.

- **Are students able to draw polygons containing only 90-degree angles that have more than four sides?** Do the polygons they draw have perimeters of 600 steps?

- **Are they able to use turns other than 90 degrees to draw a triangle with a perimeter of 600 steps?** Do they demonstrate understanding that a bigger turn creates a smaller angle and vice versa?

DIFFERENTIATION: Supporting the Range of Learners

Extension Some students may notice that all of the polygons they draw using only 90-degree turns have an even number of sides. Ask these students to consider why they think this pattern takes place and whether or not they think it is always true that polygons drawn with only 90-degree turns have an even number of sides.

DISCUSSION

③ Smallest Angle, Biggest Angle

15 MIN   CLASS

Math Focus Points for Discussion

◆ Measuring acute angles by relating them to 90 degrees

You've been working with angles of different sizes today, some smaller than 90 degrees, and some larger than 90 degrees. Here's a 90-degree angle.

Hold two rulers so that they form a 90-degree angle.

What would an angle that's smaller than 90 degrees look like?

Invite one or two students to move the rulers to show several acute angles.

What do you think is the smallest angle we could make? Talk about this with your partner for a minute.

Instruct students to see whether they can make a very small angle on their desk with two pencils. They might also try using their hands or arms to show how small an angle can be.

Students make angles that measure less than 90°.

Give students a minute or two to discuss this. The purpose here is for students to revisit how angles are created by degrees of turn as the sides, or rays, pivot from the vertex. This is an idea that they first encountered in their work with angles in Grade 3, and also with turning the turtle in the *LogoPaths* software. In this Investigation, students are working with angles that have been fixed in the polygons, so the turning motion that created the angles is not as easy to notice.

Collect students' ideas about what the smallest angle might be. Some may say that it could be one degree; others may realize that there can be fractions of a degree, and therefore an angle can keep getting smaller indefinitely as it approaches zero. As students make their arguments, have them demonstrate with the rulers, pencils, or their hands, so that the motion of "closing down" to make smaller and smaller angles is evident in the discussion.

What do you think the largest angle is? We know we can make angles that are bigger than 90 degrees, but how big? Can you show that with your pencils or your hands?

Collect students' ideas about this question also. It is likely that many students will stop at a horizontal line (180 degrees), or just shy of it. This is because it may be hard for them to visualize an angle when the vertex seems to disappear. If that is the case, show a 180-degree angle with the two rulers, and ask:

If I open this angle out so much that the two sides are now pointing in opposite directions, does it still have a vertex? Where is it? How many degrees do you think this angle is, when it looks like a horizontal line?

Collect students' ideas about this, which should include either combining two right angles to make a horizontal line, or noticing that there are two right angles within the larger angle; therefore, $90 + 90 = 180$. Then hold the two rulers up one more time.

What if I kept moving these two rulers, or the two sides of this angle, apart? Could there be an angle that's even bigger than 180 degrees? What would that look like?

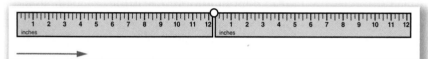

Students may have a variety of viewpoints about this. If students are very familiar with turtle turns in the *LogoPaths* computer program, they often think of angles that are greater than 180 degrees as "turning the corner." They may also refer to angles in concave figures that they have made with Power Polygons. Some may know that an angle can turn all the way around in a circle, which is 360 degrees. Give students an opportunity to explain and demonstrate their thinking. It is important that they come away from this discussion knowing that there are, in fact, angles larger than 180 degrees, since the sides of an angle can keep moving farther away from each other, just as they can keep moving closer together.

SESSION FOLLOW-UP
Daily Practice and Homework

 Daily Practice: For ongoing review, have students complete *Student Activity Book* page 44.

 Homework: On *Student Activity Book* page 45, students sort triangles by identifying the size of the angles.

 Student Math Handbook: Students and families may use *Student Math Handbook* pages 111–113 for reference and review. See pages 170–174 in the back of this unit.

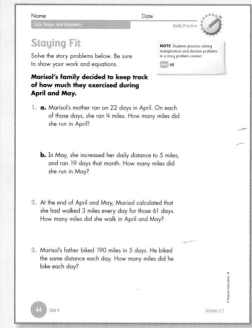

▲ Student Activity Book, p. 44

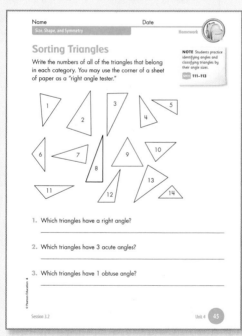

▲ Student Activity Book, p. 45

Assessment: Building Angles

Math Focus Points

◆ Using known angles to find the measure of other angles

◆ Measuring acute angles by relating them to 90 degrees

Today's Plan		Materials
① DISCUSSION **More Strategies for How Many Degrees**	🕐 15 MIN 👥 CLASS	• *Student Activity Book,* p. 39 (with Problem 1 completed; from Session 3.2)
② MATH WORKSHOP **Measuring and Building Angles** **2A** How Many Degrees? **2B** Assessment: Building Angles **2C** *LogoPaths* Activities: *600 Steps* or *800 Steps, Other Polygons* (optional)	🕐 30 MIN	**2A** • *Student Activity Book,* pp. 39–40 (from Session 3.2) **2B** • *Student Activity Book,* pp. 41–43 (from Session 3.2) • M22 ☑ * • Power Polygons **2C** • M7 (optional)* • Computers with LogoPaths software installed*
③ DISCUSSION **How Do You Know It Is 120 Degrees?**	🕐 15 MIN 👥 CLASS	
④ SESSION FOLLOW-UP **Daily Practice and Homework**		• *Student Activity Book,* pp. 47–49 • *Student Math Handbook,* pp. 111–113

*See *Materials to Prepare,* p. 87.

Ten-Minute Math

Today's Number: Broken Calculator Students create five expressions that equal 1,220. They must use addition or subtraction in their expressions. The 1 and 2 keys are broken. Have two or three students share their equations and explain how they know that the answer is correct. (Examples: $890 + 330 = 1,220$ or $5,550 - 4,330 = 1,220$)

DISCUSSION

① More Strategies for How Many Degrees

Math Focus Points for Discussion

◆ Measuring acute angles by relating them to 90 degrees

Begin by asking students to find the measurement of the angle in Problem 1 on *Student Activity Book* page 39. Allow students a minute to review their work and then ask a few students to share their ideas.

Students might say:

"I know all of the angles in the green triangle are 60 degrees because two of the little angles in shape O fit into each one and those are 30 because three of them fit into the right angle."

"I know from yesterday that the small angles in shape O are each 30. And two of those fit into it, so it is 60 degrees."

"I compared it to a 90-degree angle and saw that it is 30 degrees less than the 90, so it is 60."

As students are making their arguments and representing their thinking with the polygon pieces, encourage other students to ask questions and restate what they are hearing. Students at their desks may also use their own polygon pieces to act out what is being presented.

If students do not have a lot of ideas about how to find the measurement of this angle, encourage them to use what they already know about these angles. Ask questions like:

Look at the combinations you used to make a 90-degree angle. Since we know the two angles must equal 90 degrees, what are some combinations you can think of that have a sum of 90? Which seem reasonable for the size of these angles?

It is important that students come to an understanding of the measures of the angles because then they will have a way to recreate the visual image if they forget the actual numbers. Students should come away from this discussion knowing that the sum of the smaller (acute) angles that make up a right angle must be 90 degrees. They will continue to explore the actual measures of the angles in the next session and in computer activities throughout the year.

MATH WORKSHOP

30 MIN

② Measuring and Building Angles

In this Math Workshop, you will be assessing students on their ability to identify angles of various measures as you observe them working on building angles of 60, 120, and 150 degrees.

②A How Many Degrees?

INDIVIDUALS

For complete details about this activity, see Session 3.2, page 96.

. . . .

②B Assessment: Building Angles

INDIVIDUALS

This observed assessment addresses Benchmark 3: Know that a right angle measures 90 degrees, and use this as a landmark to find angles of 30, 45, and 60 degrees.

For this observed assessment, you will need to plan to meet individually with each student for a minute or two as they are working on *Student Activity Book* pages 41–43. Ask each student to show you an angle on a Power Polygon piece that measures each of these: 90 degrees, 30 degrees, 60 degrees, and 45 degrees. Choose one of these angles and ask the student to tell you how she knows that it measures, for example, 30 degrees.

Students might say:

"I found that I could fit three of these in the 90-degree angle, and 30 plus 30 plus 30 is 90, so one of them is 30."

Record your observations for each student on Assessment Checklist: Building Angles (M22). You may also want to jot down any notes you may need about students' understanding so that you can go back and work with those students who are unclear about these measures at a different time. If there is not enough time to get to every student in this Math Workshop, plan to meet with the remaining students either outside of math class or during the next Math Workshop in Investigation 4.

ONGOING ASSESSMENT: Observing Students at Work

Students identify angles that measure 30, 45, 60, and 90 degrees.

- **Do students correctly identify each angle?** Do they use what they know about the measure of other angles, such as a right angle, to help them find the measure of new angles?

DIFFERENTIATION: Supporting the Range of Learners

Intervention Students who can accurately identify all four angles meet the benchmark. Students who can only identify a right angle and one or two others partially meet the benchmark. Be sure that these students are clear that angles of 30, 45, and 60 degrees must all be smaller than 90 degrees. These students should spend more time finding different ways to construct right angles from smaller angles with the Power Polygon pieces.

Intervention Students who cannot correctly identify a right angle will most likely not be able to identify other angles in relation to 90 degrees, and therefore do not meet the benchmark. These students will need to practice finding right angles in objects around the classroom or at home, using a corner of a piece of paper as a "right-angle measuring tool."

2C *LogoPaths* Activities: *600 Steps* or *800 Steps, Other Polygons* (optional)

INDIVIDUALS PAIRS

Students who have not yet worked on *600 Steps* (M6) should do that activity first before moving on to *800 Steps*.

Students work alone or with partners on this *LogoPaths* activity. Using forward and backward moves and 90-degree turns, they draw polygons with more than four sides that have perimeters of 800 steps. They sketch the polygons and label the lengths of the sides on *LogoPaths: 800 Steps, Other Polygons* (M7).

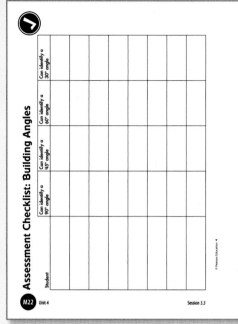

▲ Resource Masters, M22 ✓

Name _____ Date _____

Size, Shape, and Symmetry

LogoPaths: 800 Steps, Other Polygons

Use *LogoPaths Free Explore* to draw two polygons with **more than four sides** that have perimeters of 800 steps. Use **only 90° turns** in your polygons.

1. Sketch the first polygon that you drew in the space below or on the back of this sheet. Label the length of each side.

2. Sketch the second polygon that you drew in the space below or on the back of this sheet. Label the length of each side.

CHALLENGE: Use *LogoPaths Free Explore* to draw a **parallelogram** with a perimeter of 800 steps that is **not** a square or rectangle. Use the *Turtle Turner* to help you decide what turning angles you need to enter. Record your commands and sketch the parallelogram you drew on the back of this sheet. Label the length of each side.

Unit 4 M7

▲ Resource Masters, M7

After completing these two polygons, students are challenged to draw a nonrectangular quadrilateral with a perimeter of 800 steps. This challenge requires students to use turns other than 90 degrees and to consider the relationship between the turning angles and the interior angles of the quadrilateral created by each turn.

ONGOING ASSESSMENT: Observing Students at Work

Students use their understanding of perimeter and the structure of polygons to create different nonrectangular figures with perimeters of 800 steps.

- **Are students able to draw polygons containing only 90-degree angles that have more than four sides?** Do the polygons they draw have perimeters of 800 steps?

- **Are they able to use turns other than 90 degrees to draw a nonrectangular quadrilateral with a perimeter of 800 steps?** Do they demonstrate understanding that a bigger turn creates a smaller angle and vice versa?

DIFFERENTIATION: Supporting the Range of Learners

Extension Students who have successfully drawn triangles and quadrilaterals with perimeters of 600 and 800 steps can be challenged to draw additional triangles and quadrilaterals with those perimeters.

 DISCUSSION

15 MIN   CLASS

③ How Do You Know It Is 120 Degrees?

Math Focus Points for Discussion

◆ Using known angles to find the measure of other angles

Bring the class together and ask several students to share how they found angles that equal 120 degrees.

Students might say:

 "I know what a 90-degree angle looks like. I know that a 60 and a 30 equal 90. So if I add another 30 to that, it equals 120 degrees."

 "I used the 90-degree and 30-degree angles together to find the 120. Then I used those to find that the G polygon has two 120-degree angles."

 "I put four 30-degree angles (on shape O) together to make 120, because 4 times 30 is 120."

 "I already found out that polygon N has 60-degree angles. Two of them fit together to make the larger angle in J, so it's 60 plus 60 or 120 degrees."

Ask students to demonstrate each of their strategies with the Power Polygon pieces that they used. As students offer their explanations, ask other students to repeat the argument or to ask questions about it.

Students use their own polygon pieces to act out what is being presented.

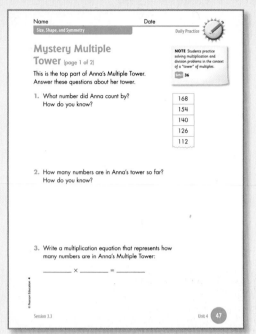

▲ **Student Activity Book, p. 47**

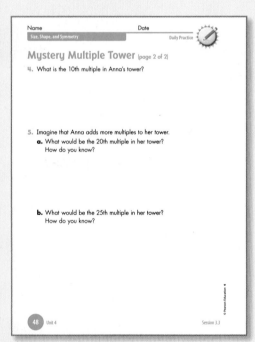

▲ **Student Activity Book, p. 48**

4 Daily Practice and Homework

 Daily Practice: For ongoing review, have students complete *Student Activity Book* pages 47–48.

 Homework: On *Student Activity Book* page 49, students use a 90-degree angle and a 45-degree angle to identify the measure of other angles.

 Student Math Handbook: Students and families may use *Student Math Handbook* pages 111–113 for reference and review. See pages 170–174 in the back of this unit.

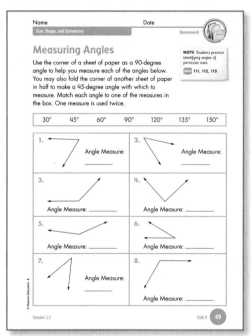

▲ **Student Activity Book, p. 49**

Mathematical Emphasis

Area Measurement Finding and understanding area

Math Focus Points

◆ Finding the area of symmetrical designs

◆ Understanding that the larger the unit of area, the smaller the number of units needed to measure the area

◆ Dividing irregular polygons into two shapes that have equal area

◆ Finding the area of polygons by decomposing shapes

◆ Finding the area of polygons using square units

◆ Finding the area of rectangles

◆ Finding the area of triangles in relation to the area of rectangles

This Investigation also focuses on

◆ Making designs with mirror symmetry

Finding Area

	Student Activity Book	Student Math Handbook	Professional Development: Read Ahead of Time	
SESSION 4.1 p. 112				
Symmetry Students make symmetrical designs from given polygons (triangles, trapezoids, hexagons, and rhombuses). They measure the area of their designs using the triangle as the unit of measure.	51–54	116–117		
SESSION 4.2 p. 116				
Symmetry and Area Students continue to measure area with nonsquare units of measure (triangles and trapezoids). They discuss how different units of measure yield different results.	55–57	116–117		
SESSION 4.3 p. 121				
Finding Halves of Crazy Cakes Students divide nonrectangular polygons in half. They use the *LogoPaths* software to measure turns in degrees (optional).	58–61	54	• **Dialogue Box:** Dividing Crazy Cakes, p. 168	
SESSION 4.4 p. 127				
Decomposing Shapes Students use geoboards to find the area of different shapes, including a focus on finding the area of a triangle.	58–59, 63–66	114–115		
SESSION 4.5 p. 135				
Area of Rectangles Students discuss how they found the area of shapes on the geoboard, including the area of triangles. They also find the area of partially covered rectangles.	63–64, 67–69	114–115		
SESSION 4.6 p. 141				
Area of Polygons Students find the area of different polygons by decomposing shapes into rectangles and triangles.	67, 70–74	114–115		
SESSION 4.7 p. 146				
End-of-Unit Assessment Students are assessed on their understanding of the properties of quadrilaterals and the size of various landmark angles, and the ability to find the area of a given polygon.	75	107–116	• **Teacher Note:** End-of-Unit Assessment, p. 159	

Ten-Minute Math See page 16 for an overview.

Quick Images: 2-D

- T43–44, *Quick Images: 2-D* 🖨 Set aside images 11–18 for this investigation.
- **No materials needed**

Today's Number: Broken Calculator

- **No materials needed**

Materials to Gather	Materials to Prepare
• **T49, Triangle Paper** 🖨 • **Power Polygons** (2 sets) • **Crayons, colored pencils, or markers** (as needed) • **Small hand mirrors** (as needed; optional)	• **M23, Triangle Paper** Make copies. (50 copies)
• **Power Polygons** (as needed)	• **M23, Triangle Paper** Make copies. (1 per student; from Session 4.1)
• **T50, Crazy Cake #1** 🖨	• **Computers with** *LogoPaths* **software installed** (optional)
• **T51, Geoboard Dot Paper** 🖨 (optional) • **T52, Crazy Cake #6** 🖨 • **Geoboards** (1 per student) • **Rubber bands** (as needed) • **Overhead Geoboard** (optional)	• **Computers with** *LogoPaths* **software installed** (optional)
• **T51, Geoboard Dot Paper** 🖨 (from Session 4.4; optional) • **Overhead Geoboard** (optional) • **Rubber bands** (as needed) • **Geoboards** (1 per student)	• **Computers with** *LogoPaths* **software installed** (optional)
• **Power Polygon piece L** (2 per student)	• **M27–M28, End-of-Unit Assessment** Make copies. (1 per student)

🖨 Overhead Transparency

Symmetry

Math Focus Points

◆ Making designs with mirror symmetry

◆ Finding the area of symmetrical designs

Today's Plan		Materials
ACTIVITY **① Symmetry with Power Polygons**	40 MIN PAIRS	• *Student Activity Book,* p. 51 • T49 ; M23* • Power Polygons; crayons, colored pencils, or markers; small hand mirrors (optional)
DISCUSSION **② Symmetry**	10 MIN CLASS GROUPS	• Students' symmetrical designs (from Activity 1)
ACTIVITY **③ Finding Area**	10 MIN PAIRS	• *Student Activity Book,* p. 52
SESSION FOLLOW-UP **④ Daily Practice and Homework**		• *Student Activity Book,* pp. 53–54 • *Student Math Handbook,* pp. 116–117

*See *Materials to Prepare,* p. 111.

Ten-Minute Math

Quick Images: 2-D Show Images 11 and 12 (one at a time) from *Quick Images: 2-D* (T43) and follow the procedure for the basic routine. For each image, students discuss how they drew their figures, including any revisions that they made after each viewing. Ask students:

- How did you remember the parts of the image?
- What did you notice about the relationship of the parts of the image?
- What helped you remember the whole image so that you could draw your design?

ACTIVITY

1 Symmetry with Power Polygons

40 MIN   PAIRS

Distribute sets of Power Polygons. Students use the hexagon, equilateral triangle, trapezoid, and blue parallelogram for this activity (pieces H, N, K, M). They should put the other shapes aside for now. ❶

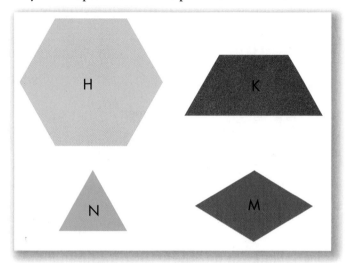

On the overhead projector display Triangle Paper (T49) while you demonstrate how to do the activity.

Today you'll be making two **symmetrical** designs with your partner, and if you have time, one design that is not symmetrical. ❷

Make a horizontal line across the transparency about halfway down the page—on one of the horizontal lines of the graphic. Place one of the shapes so it shares an edge with the line of symmetry. ❸

If we were going to make a symmetrical design, what block should we put on the other side of the line, and where should we put it?

Call a student up to place the shape, and make sure everyone agrees it is the correct shape in the correct place. Students may initially be confused about placing a block so that it is a mirror image. Place a few more blocks to make certain students understand the idea that they are making a shape where the two halves are a reflection of each other. If they drew the shape on paper and folded it in half (on the line of symmetry) the shapes on each side would match. Students can also use small hand mirrors to show symmetry.

Briefly review the directions on *Student Activity Book* page 51 with students, and answer any questions students may have. Students work with a partner to complete a design on copies of Triangle Paper (M23).

Math Note

❶ **Limiting the Set of Shapes** For this activity, students are limited to Power Polygon pieces N, K, M, H, because they will be using these shapes to think about area relationships after they build designs. In this set of shapes, if the small green triangle is considered the unit of area measurement, then the blue rhombus equals two triangles, the red trapezoid equals three triangles, and the yellow hexagon equals six triangles. Students should be familiar with these relationships from their work with pattern blocks in earlier grades.

Differentiation

❷ **English Language Learners** To help English Language Learners learn vocabulary associated with the concept of *symmetry,* you can preview this concept in a small group. Take a piece of notebook paper and fold it in half. Are the two *halves* of this rectangle the same or different? They're the same, so we can say that this shape is *symmetrical.* Do you see where the *fold* is? That's called the *line of symmetry.* To assess students' grasp of this vocabulary, show several other shapes and ask students to determine whether or not they are *symmetrical.* Have students explain their answers using the vocabulary you just reviewed.

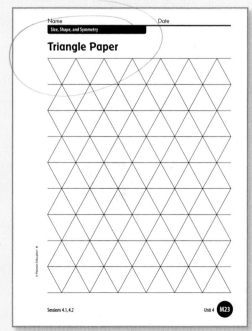

▲ **Resource Masters, M23; T49**

Math Notes

❸ Fourth Graders and Line Symmetry It is expected that fourth graders know what line symmetry is. If students are unsure about this type of symmetry, the following group work should help. If necessary, tell them that one way to know whether a design is symmetrical is that if you fold the design in half, the shapes will match up. You might also choose to look for examples in the classroom of things that are symmetrical and things that are not.

❹ Standard vs. Nonstandard Units of Measure Similar to any type of measurement, area has to be measured using an area unit. The standard unit for measuring area is a square unit. Students will use square units later in this Investigation to measure the area of polygons. However, it is important for students to understand that regardless of the shape of the unit being used, area can only be accurately measured by completely covering the space within a figure with that unit.

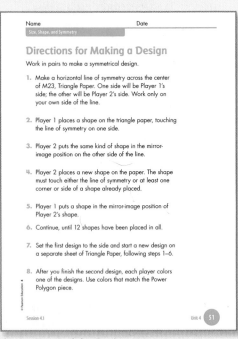

▲ **Student Activity Book, p. 51**

ONGOING ASSESSMENT: Observing Students at Work

Students work together to build a design with mirror symmetry.

- **Can students create a symmetrical design?**

DISCUSSION

② Symmetry

10 MIN   CLASS   GROUPS

Math Focus Points for Discussion

◆ Making designs with mirror symmetry

Take a few minutes to share your designs in your small group. If we say something has symmetry, *what do we mean? Talk to your neighbor about this.*

Give students a minute or two to discuss their designs, and then collect responses to the question about symmetry.

We know all our designs have at least one line of symmetry. Look at your designs. Do they have more than one line of symmetry?

Give students a minute or two to consider this. Many of the designs will also have a vertical line of symmetry, and may also have other lines. Ask the group to come back together, and ask students to share examples of other lines of symmetry. If necessary, have them fold the design in half to show that it is symmetrical. Students can also use small hand mirrors to show symmetry.

ACTIVITY

③ Finding Area

10 MIN   PAIRS

Let's say we wanted to measure one of our designs. What are some ways we could measure the design?

Collect a few answers. Students may suggest measuring the length, width, perimeter, or area.

*One way we could measure this design is to find its area. Area is the amount of space (surface) an object covers. We measure the area by using a unit of measure that will cover the surface of the object. Let's say that this small green triangle is our unit of measure. How many of these triangles do you think it would take to cover one of the designs you just made?*❹

Choose one student's design to hold up. Briefly collect a few responses. Students then work in pairs on *Student Activity Book* page 52 to find the area of their designs using the triangle as their unit of measure. Each student records the pair's findings on his/her own sheet.

ONGOING ASSESSMENT: Observing Students at Work

Students find the area of their symmetrical designs.

- **Do students understand that area is the measure of the whole surface of the design?**

- **How do students find the area?** Do they completely cover their design with triangles and count the triangles? Do they use the relationships between the Power Polygon pieces to find the total number of triangles?

- **Do students use the symmetry of their designs to help them find the area, by finding the area on one side of the line of symmetry and then doubling that?**

SESSION FOLLOW-UP
Daily Practice and Homework

 Daily Practice: For ongoing review, have students complete *Student Activity Book* page 53.

 Homework: Students look for lines of symmetry in letters of the alphabet on *Student Activity Book* page 54.

 Student Math Handbook: Students and families may use *Student Math Handbook* pages 116–117 for reference and review. See pages 170–174 in the back of this unit.

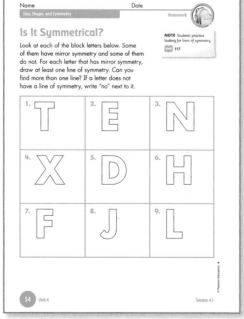

Name ___ Date ___
Size, Shape, and Symmetry | Homework

Is It Symmetrical?

Look at each of the block letters below. Some of them have mirror symmetry and some of them do not. For each letter that has mirror symmetry, draw at least one line of symmetry. Can you find more than one line? If a letter does not have a line of symmetry, write "no" next to it.

NOTE Students practice looking for lines of symmetry.

1. T 2. E 3. N
4. X 5. D 6. H
7. F 8. J 9. L

54 Unit 4 Session 4.1

▲ Student Activity Book, p. 54

Name ___ Date ___
Size, Shape, and Symmetry

Measuring Area with Triangles

Using the triangle piece, determine the area of each of the designs that you made. How many triangles does it take to cover the design?

1. Look at your first design. What is its area? ___

   Explain how you determined its area.

2. Look at your second design. What is its area? ___

   Explain how you determined its area.

52 Unit 4 Session 4.1

▲ Student Activity Book, p. 52 *WRITING*

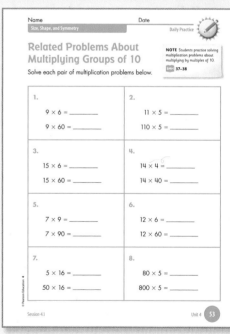

Name ___ Date ___
Size, Shape, and Symmetry | Daily Practice

Related Problems About Multiplying Groups of 10

Solve each pair of multiplication problems below.

NOTE Students practice solving multiplication problems about multiplying by multiples of 10.
37–38

1. $9 \times 6 =$ ___ $9 \times 60 =$ ___	2. $11 \times 5 =$ ___ $110 \times 5 =$ ___
3. $15 \times 6 =$ ___ $15 \times 60 =$ ___	4. $14 \times 4 =$ ___ $14 \times 40 =$ ___
5. $7 \times 9 =$ ___ $7 \times 90 =$ ___	6. $12 \times 6 =$ ___ $12 \times 60 =$ ___
7. $5 \times 16 =$ ___ $50 \times 16 =$ ___	8. $80 \times 5 =$ ___ $800 \times 5 =$ ___

Session 4.1 Unit 4 53

▲ Student Activity Book, p. 53

Symmetry and Area

Math Focus Points

- Finding the area of symmetrical designs
- Understanding that the larger the unit of area, the smaller the number of units needed to measure the area

Today's Plan		Materials
① DISCUSSION **Area of Designs**	20 MIN CLASS	• M23 (from Session 4.1) • Power Polygons
② ACTIVITY **Area of More Shapes**	30 MIN INDIVIDUALS	• *Student Activity Book*, pp. 55–56 • Power Polygons
③ DISCUSSION **Comparing Units of Measure**	10 MIN CLASS	• *Student Activity Book*, pp. 55–56 (completed, from Activity 2)
④ SESSION FOLLOW-UP **Daily Practice**		• *Student Activity Book*, p. 57 • *Student Math Handbook*, pp. 116–117

Ten-Minute Math

Quick Images: 2-D Show Images 13 and 14 (one at a time) from *Quick Images: 2-D* (T44) and follow the procedure for the basic routine. For each image, students discuss how they drew their figures, including any revisions that they made after each viewing. Ask students:

- How did you remember the parts of the image?
- What did you notice about the relationship of the parts of the image?
- What helped you remember the whole image so that you could build your design?

① DISCUSSION

Area of Designs

Math Focus Points for Discussion

◆ Finding the area of symmetrical designs

Yesterday you used the triangle piece to find the area of the design that you and your partner made. Many of your measurements were different because you were each measuring different designs. Today we're all going to build the same design and talk about its area.

Using the Power Polygon pieces, build this design on the overhead:

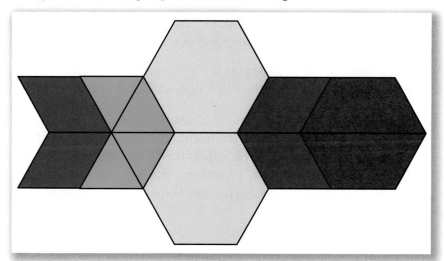

We're going to use the triangle again as our unit of measure to find the area of this design. With your partner, build this design and then decide how many of these triangles it would take to cover the whole design.

Give students five minutes or so to do this. Ask for students to share answers and to explain how they figured it out.

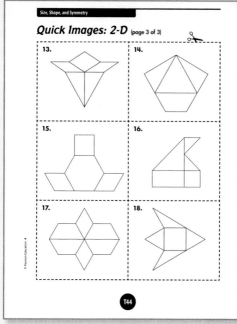

▲ Transparencies, T44

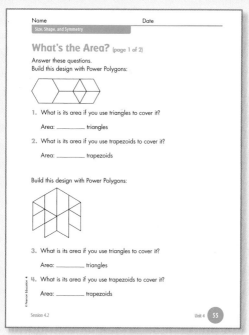

▲ Student Activity Book, p. 55

Math Note

❶ Congruence 2-D figures are considered *congruent* if they are the same size and shape. Figures can be flipped, turned, or slid to prove whether or not shapes are congruent. Congruent shapes have the same area. (However, shapes with the same area may or may not be congruent.)

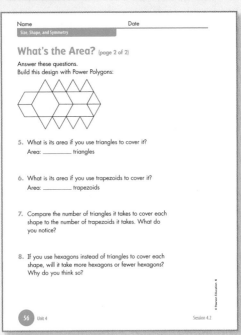

Name _____ Date _____

Size, Shape, and Symmetry

What's the Area? (page 2 of 2)

Answer these questions.
Build this design with Power Polygons:

5. What is its area if you use triangles to cover it?
   Area: _____ triangles

6. What is its area if you use trapezoids to cover it?
   Area: _____ trapezoids

7. Compare the number of triangles it takes to cover each shape to the number of trapezoids it takes. What do you notice?

8. If you use hexagons instead of triangles to cover each shape, will it take more hexagons or fewer hexagons? Why do you think so?

56   Unit 4   Session 4.2

▲ **Student Activity Book, p. 56**

Students might say:

"We built the design on the triangle paper and outlined it. Then we counted how many triangles there were. It was 30."

"We used what we knew about the pieces. It takes two triangles to make a rhombus—there's 4 rhombuses so that's 8 triangles. Two hexagons is 12 triangles. Two trapezoids is 6 triangles, and then there's just 4 triangles. So 8 plus 12 is 20, 6 and 4 is 10, so there's 30."

If no student brings up the idea of using symmetry to find the total, do so yourself. Cover the bottom half of the design.

How would finding the area of the top half of the design help me determine the area of the whole design? Talk to your partner.

Give students time to discuss their answers, and then ask them for their ideas. One argument you might hear is that because the figure is symmetrical, the shapes that appear both above and below the line of symmetry are congruent.❶ Another is that since the two shapes are congruent, they can double the area of the top half to find the area of the entire shape.

ACTIVITY

2 Area of More Shapes

30 MIN   INDIVIDUALS

Direct students' attention to *Student Activity Book* pages 55–56. Students may work with a partner to complete this task, but each student records on an individual sheet.

ONGOING ASSESSMENT: Observing Students at Work

Students find the area of given designs, using the triangle and then the trapezoid as the unit of measure.

- **How do students determine area?** Do they build with all triangles? Do they use the relationship between the shapes (e.g., it takes two triangles to make the rhombus, or six triangles to make the hexagon) to find the area?

- **What challenges does using the trapezoid as the unit of area cause?** Do students use the relationship between the triangle and trapezoid (it takes three triangles to make the trapezoid) to find the area? Do they recognize that it takes fewer trapezoids to cover the shape?

- **How do students make sense of a measurement that is not all whole units ($6\frac{2}{3}$ trapezoids for Problem 4)?** Do they use fractions, or consider the extra two triangles as "left over"?

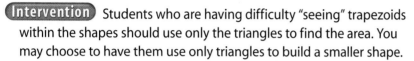

DIFFERENTIATION: Supporting the Range of Learners

Intervention Students who are having difficulty "seeing" trapezoids within the shapes should use only the triangles to find the area. You may choose to have them use only triangles to build a smaller shape.

Extension Other students might be challenged to find the area using each shape (hexagon, trapezoid, parallelogram, and triangle) as the unit of area.

DISCUSSION

③ Comparing Units of Measure

10 MIN   CLASS

Math Focus Points for Discussion

◆ Understanding that the larger the unit of area, the smaller the number of units needed to measure the area

Briefly go over the answers to Problems 1–6 on *Student Activity Book* pages 55–56, making sure that students agree how many triangles and trapezoids it takes to cover each shape. (The first design takes 18 triangles and 6 trapezoids. The second design takes 20 triangles and $6\frac{2}{3}$ trapezoids. The third design takes 30 triangles and 10 trapezoids.)

Ask a few students to explain how they got their answers. Briefly discuss the number of trapezoids for Problem 2, as the answer contains a fraction. If students say that the area is six trapezoids and two triangles, ask them what fractional part of the trapezoid is covered by the two triangles.

What did you notice about the numbers of triangles it takes, and the number of trapezoids it takes? Why does it take fewer trapezoids than triangles?

Math Note

❷ Fractions of a Unit The second design cannot be completely covered by trapezoids. However, since students are finding area, all the space must be counted. Three triangles cover one trapezoid, so two triangles would cover $\frac{2}{3}$ of the trapezoid.

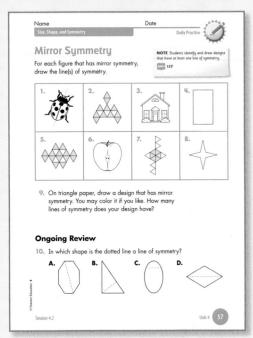

▲ Student Activity Book, p. 57

Students might say:

 "It took 3 times as many triangles, because it takes 3 triangles to make a trapezoid."

 "The trapezoids are bigger so it takes fewer of them."

If time remains, ask students about the hexagon: how many hexagons would cover the design; how they know; and the relationship between the hexagon and the trapezoid ($\frac{1}{2}$ of the hexagon), and the hexagon and the triangle ($\frac{1}{6}$ of the hexagon.)❷

SESSION FOLLOW-UP

4 Daily Practice

Daily Practice: For ongoing review of this unit's content, have students complete *Student Activity Book* page 57.

Student Math Handbook: Students and families may use *Student Math Handbook* pages 116–117 for reference and review. See pages 170–174 in the back of this unit.

Finding Halves of Crazy Cakes

Math Focus Points

◆ Dividing irregular polygons into two shapes that have equal area

◆ Finding the area of polygons by decomposing shapes

Today's Plan		Materials
ACTIVITY **①Introducing Crazy Cakes**	🕐 15 MIN · 👤 INDIVIDUALS · 👥 CLASS	• *Student Activity Book,* pp. 58–59 • T50 💻
ACTIVITY **②*LogoPaths* Activity: Introducing *Mazes* (optional)**	👥 GROUPS · 👥 CLASS	• Computers with *LogoPaths* software installed*
MATH WORKSHOP **③Finding Area** **3A** Crazy Cakes **3B** *LogoPaths* Activity: *Mazes* (optional)	🕐 45 MIN	**3A** • *Student Activity Book,* pp. 58–59 (from Activity 1) **3B** • Computers with *LogoPaths* software installed*
SESSION FOLLOW-UP **④Daily Practice and Homework**		• *Student Activity Book,* pp. 60–61 • *Student Math Handbook,* p. 54

*See *Materials to Prepare,* p. 111.

Ten-Minute Math

Quick Images: 2-D Show Images 15 and 16 (one at a time) from *Quick Images: 2-D* (T44) and follow the procedure for the basic routine. For each image, students discuss how they drew their figures, including any revisions that they made after each viewing. Ask students:

• How did you remember the parts of the image?

• What did you notice about the relationship of the parts of the image?

• What helped you remember the whole image so that you could draw your design?

Professional Development

❶ Dialogue Box: Dividing Crazy Cakes, p. 168

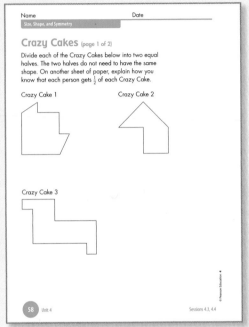

▲ Student Activity Book, p. 58

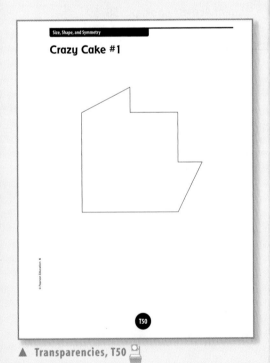

▲ Transparencies, T50

ACTIVITY

① Introducing Crazy Cakes

15 MIN INDIVIDUALS CLASS

Tell students to look at Crazy Cake #1 on *Student Activity Book* page 58. Display Crazy Cake #1 (T50) on the overhead.

Let's say that this is a cake that two people are going to share equally. We'll call it a "crazy cake" because the shape is unusual for a cake! How could you cut it to show that each person gets exactly half of the cake? You have to be able to explain how you know that each piece is the same size.❶

Give students a few minutes to work alone or with a partner to divide the first crazy cake on their student sheet (which is the same on the transparency) in half. Call on students to come to the overhead and show how they divided the crazy cake.

Students use a wide variety of strategies to solve this problem. Two likely strategies include:

- Drawing a line to show mirror symmetry: "Since both pieces are the same, they have to be equal, or half."

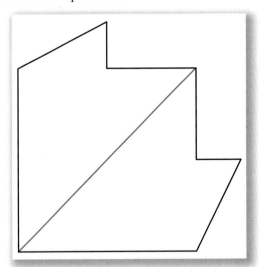

- Drawing a line and comparing the area of the shapes on either side of the line: "This rectangle and this rectangle are the same, and these two triangles are the same. So both sides are one half!"

If no student suggests the second idea listed above, ask whether they see any smaller shapes within the whole shape that can help them divide the shape into two parts with equal area. Since not all the Crazy Cakes have a line of symmetry that can be used, this is an important idea to introduce.

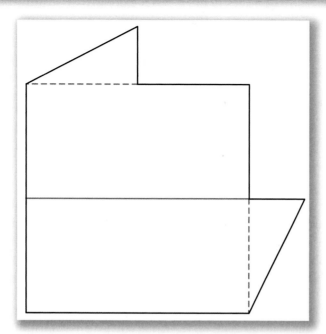

Sometimes we can use a line of symmetry to divide the shapes in half, but sometimes the shapes don't have a line of symmetry. One thing you can do is two find smaller shapes within the whole shape that "match up." The other thing you can do is think about moving some of the smaller shapes around to make a shape that is symmetrical.

ACTIVITY

GROUPS   CLASS

② *LogoPaths* Activity: Introducing *Mazes* (optional)

Mazes is a more complex version of *Feed the Turtle,* an activity which students played in Grade 3. In both *LogoPaths* activities, students move a turtle through a maze to collect food at various locations. In *Feed the Turtle,* students were limited to forward and backward steps in multiples of 10 and right and left turns in multiples of 30 degrees. In *Mazes,* they are able to move forward and backward and turn without these limitations (though students will discover that solutions generally involve moves in multiples of ten turtle steps and turns in multiples of ten degrees). Both activities help students develop familiarity with degrees as a way of measuring turns—for example, there are 90 degrees in a quarter turn, a half turn or reverse in direction is 180 degrees, etc. The games also help them develop and compare visual images of turning angles.

Open *Mazes* in the *LogoPaths* software and select the level 1 activity.

The activity I'm teaching you today is called *Mazes*. It's a lot like the activity *Feed the Turtle*, which you've played before. Your job is to help the turtle get to the food in the maze before it runs out of energy. In *Feed the Turtle*, you can only use multiples of 10 for all the forward and backward moves, and multiples of 30 for all the right and left turns. In *Mazes*, you can enter commands to move forward or backward or turn any amount. Just like in *Feed the Turtle*, every time the turtle eats, it fills up its energy. You want to have enough energy to get to the next prize and finish the activity, so make sure you plan the order in which the turtle eats the food carefully.

Turn the turtle left or right 90 degrees. Then, using students' suggestions for the forward distance, move the turtle to the first turn in Mazes. Point out the importance of being in the middle of an intersection before making a turn in order to avoid running into a wall.

When you played *Feed the Turtle*, you could turn left or right in multiples of 30 degrees. In this activity, you can use any multiple of 10 or even numbers in between. It's helpful to think about 90 degrees as your benchmark when you try to figure out how much to turn.

Look at where the turtle is in the maze. It needs to turn right to get the food, so I'm going to type in the command for a right turn [**RT**]. Does the turtle need to turn right *more* than 90 degrees or *less* than 90 degrees?

Elicit student suggestions and demonstrate them on the computer (i.e., **RT 120 OR RT 150**). Help students understand that determining turning angles will take time and repeated experiences.

Many of you thought that we needed to turn the turtle 120 degrees, when the turn was actually 150 degrees. Don't worry if you're not getting the correct turns right away. You'll get better at being able to identify the turning angles the more you play this game.

Show students how to use the Turtle Turner ⊶ tool.

If you really feel stuck, you can use the Turtle Turner tool to help you. Select the tool. Then place the cursor where you want to go and click the mouse button. The Turtle Turner will tell you what turning angle is needed to face toward this point. However, you should always try to figure out the turning angle before using this tool. And remember, the more you play, the better you'll get.

MATH WORKSHOP

③ Finding Area

45 MIN

Students continue working on Crazy Cakes and playing *Mazes*. There are five levels in the *Mazes* activity. Tell students to do levels 1 through 3 in this session's Math Workshop.

③A Crazy Cakes

INDIVIDUALS

Students continue to work on *Student Activity Book* page 59. They examine a shape and decide how they can divide it into equal parts so that each part has equal area.

ONGOING ASSESSMENT: Observing Students at Work

Students divide nonrectangular shapes into halves with equal area.

- **How do students approach the task?** Do they decompose the shape into smaller shapes (rectangles, triangles, etc.) and then compare the size of those shapes? Do they cut the shapes apart and reconfigure them?

- **Do students use congruence or symmetry in their explanations?** For example: "These smaller shapes are all the same, so the two pieces must be equal," or "The two sides are symmetrical, so they are each half of the cake."

DIFFERENTIATION: Supporting the Range of Learners

(**Intervention**) Some students may complete only one or two of the problems, and others will complete all of the problems. If some students have difficulty seeing smaller shapes inside the Crazy Cake, ask them whether they see any triangles or rectangles they could use.

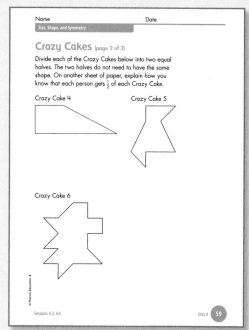

▲ **Student Activity Book, p. 59**

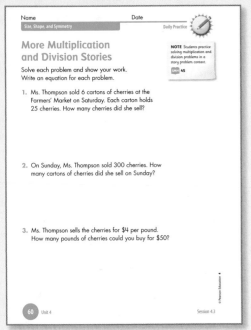

▲ **Student Activity Book, p. 60**

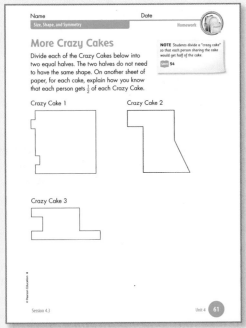

▲ **Student Activity Book, p. 61**

3B *LogoPaths* Activity: *Mazes* (optional)

INDIVIDUALS   PAIRS

Students work alone or with partners on levels 1 through 3 of this *LogoPaths* activity in which students use combinations of turns and forward and backward commands to move turtles through mazes. Students are given a certain amount of "energy" at the start of each level. The energy runs down for each move or turn command, but gets restored each time the turtle is successfully moved to a location with food. Students can try to combine commands if they run out of energy before reaching a new food item. The goal for each level is to collect all the food items before the turtle runs out of energy.

ONGOING ASSESSMENT: Observing Students at Work

Students use combinations of forward and backward moves and turns to move the turtle to given locations along a maze.

- **Can students use *LogoPaths* commands fluently?**

- **Do they use right and left turns consistently even when the turtle is not facing straight up?**

- **Do students recognize a turn of 90 degrees?** Can they accurately determine whether a turn is greater than or less than 90 degrees? Are students able to accurately determine other turning angles (30 degrees, 40 degrees, 60 degrees, 110 degrees, 150 degrees)?

- **Do students combine moves or turns to use less energy?**

- **How do they generate commands to reverse a path?** Do they realize that they can reverse previous moves and turns?

- **Do students use turns of 180 degrees to reverse direction?**

SESSION FOLLOW-UP

4 Daily Practice and Homework

 Daily Practice: For ongoing review, have students complete *Student Activity Book* page 60.

 Homework: Students solve more Crazy Cake problems on *Student Activity Book* page 61.

 Student Math Handbook: Students and families may use *Student Math Handbook* page 54 for reference and review. See pages 170–174 in the back of this unit.

Decomposing Shapes

Math Focus Points

◆ Finding the area of polygons using square units

◆ Finding the area of polygons by decomposing shapes

◆ Dividing irrregular polygons into two shapes that have equal area

Vocabulary
square unit
pentagon

Today's Plan		Materials
ACTIVITY ❶ **Introducing Area on Geoboards**	20 MIN CLASS	• T51 (optional) • Geoboards; rubber bands (as needed); overhead Geoboard (optional)
MATH WORKSHOP ❷ **Finding Area** ⓐ Crazy Cakes ⓑ *LogoPaths* Activity: *Mazes* (optional) ⓒ Measuring Area on Geoboards	25 MIN	ⓐ • *Student Activity Book,* pp. 58–59 (from Session 4.3) ⓑ • Computers with *LogoPaths* software installed* ⓒ • *Student Activity Book,* pp. 63–64 • Geoboards; rubber bands
DISCUSSION ❸ **Crazy Cakes**	15 MIN CLASS	• T52 • *Student Activity Book,* p. 59 (completed; from Activity 1)
SESSION FOLLOW-UP ❹ **Daily Practice and Homework**		• *Student Activity Book,* pp. 65–66 • *Student Math Handbook,* pp. 114–115

*See *Materials to Prepare,* p. 111.

Ten-Minute Math

Quick Images: 2-D Show Images 17 and 18 (one at a time) from *Quick Images: 2-D* (T44) and follow the procedure for the basic routine. For each image, students discuss how they drew their figures, including any revisions that they made after each viewing. Ask students:

• How did you remember the parts of the image?

• What did you notice about the relationship of the parts of the image?

• What helped you remember the whole image so that you could draw your design?

① **Introducing Geoboards** Before passing out the Geoboards, discuss with students how to use them (e.g., that rubber bands are to stay on the boards). If students have not used Geoboards before, give them five minutes to explore making shapes (such as triangles and quadrilaterals) before beginning the activity.

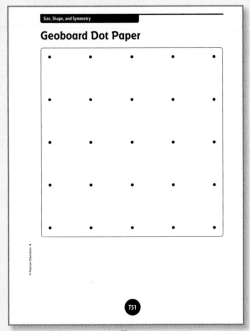

Size, Shape, and Symmetry

Geoboard Dot Paper

T51

▲ Transparencies, T51

ACTIVITY

1 Introducing Area on Geoboards

20 MIN   CLASS

Up to this point, students have been comparing the area of polygons using nonsquare units of measure. Using the Geoboards introduces square units as a standard unit for measuring area.①

Model for students how the Geoboard can be used to think about area. First, show students the large square that can be made by placing a large rubber band around all the outside pins.

This is the largest square you can make on the Geoboard. We want to find the area of this large square.

Make a small square with rubber bands on the overhead Geoboard or draw the square on Geoboard Dot Paper (T51).

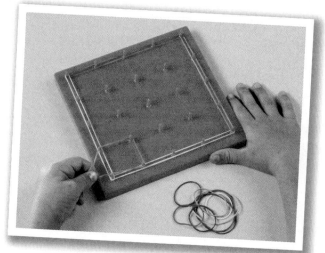

Students use a Geoboard to think about area.

Suppose we count this small square as one square unit. How many of these small squares are there on the whole Geoboard? In other words, what's the area in square units of the large square on the Geoboard?

Give students time to find and discuss the area of the Geoboard, which is 16 square units.

Either on an overhead Geoboard or by using Geoboard Dot Paper (T51), make the following shape:

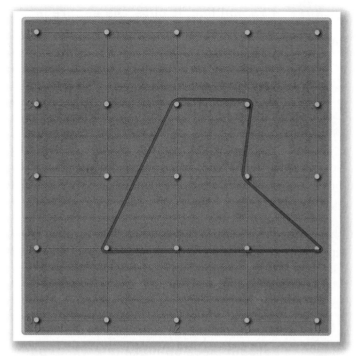

Ask students to build this shape on their Geoboards.

What is the name of this shape? [**pentagon**] What is the area, in square units, of this pentagon? Discuss the answer that you get with a neighbor.

Give students a few minutes to do this, and then call on students to have a discussion about the area of the two triangles in the figure. Highlight the two triangles by outlining each one.

A few days ago, we measured the area of some polygons using a triangle as a unit of measure. Now, we are using a square as one unit, which is a standard unit of measure for area. To do that, we have to think about how the area of these triangles relate to the area of one square. So let's start by talking about the area of each triangle. Who wants to explain what they think the area of the small triangle is?

Students had experience in Grade 3 in explaining the area of the $\frac{1}{2}$ square unit triangle. *(The triangle on the right of the pentagon.)* While it will seem obvious to many students that the area of the small triangle is $\frac{1}{2}$ square unit, make certain that they are able to explain why.

Students might say:

 "If you have the whole square unit, and draw a diagonal line, it cuts the square into half. The two triangles are congruent, so they each have an area of one-half square unit."

 "If you had two triangles like this and put them together, they make a whole square. So each triangle is one-half square unit."

Now let's talk about the area on the larger triangle on the left side of the pentagon. Who wants to explain what they think the area of this triangle is?

This is also an idea students encountered in Grade 3. Possible student explanations include:

Students might say:

 "If you cut the triangle (on the "line" of the Geoboard pegs), the top piece will fit next to the bottom piece to make one whole square unit."

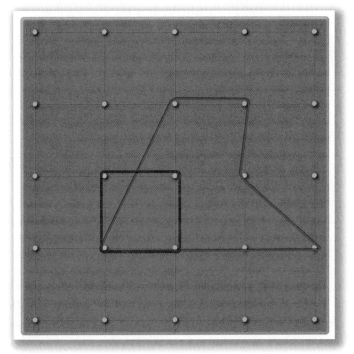

"It's sort of the same idea as the little triangle. If you make a rectangle around the triangle, you can see the line cuts the rectangle in half, so each triangle is one-half the area of the rectangle. The rectangle has an area of two square units, so the triangle has an area of one square unit."

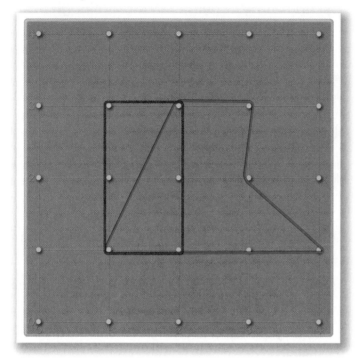

Does everyone agree that the area of this pentagon is three and one-half square units? During our Math Workshop today you'll solve more problems like this one. Thinking about the relationship between triangles and rectangles will help you.

MATH WORKSHOP

25 MIN

2 Finding Area

Students continue the Math Workshop from Session 4.3. If you are using the *LogoPaths* software, students should finish levels 1 through 3 of the *Mazes* activity sometime during this session's Math Workshop. The activity Measuring Area on the Geoboard is added to the workshop. Let students know they will be discussing their solution to Problem 6 on *Student Activity Book* pages 58–59 at the end of this session.

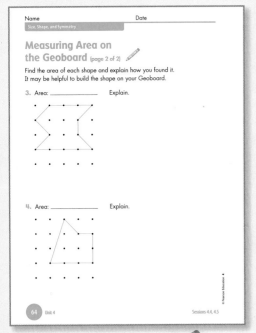

▲ Student Activity Book, p. 63

▲ Student Activity Book, p. 64

2A Crazy Cakes

INDIVIDUALS

For a full description of this activity, see Session 4.3, pages 122–123. Some students might find it useful, if possible, to build a similar Crazy Cake on the Geoboard and use that to help them divide the Crazy Cake in half.

2B *LogoPaths* Activity: *Mazes* (optional)

PAIRS **INDIVIDUALS**

For a full description of this activity, see Session 4.3, pages 123–124.

2C Measuring Area on Geoboards

INDIVIDUALS

Students complete *Student Activity Book* page 63. They discuss their solutions to Problem 2 at the beginning of Session 4.5.

ONGOING ASSESSMENT: Observing Students at Work

Students find the area of polygons.

- **How do students find area?** Do they count individual square units? How do they count the triangles?

- **Do students decompose shapes into smaller (but not individual square units) to find area?**

- **Do they use half of a rectangle to compute the area of the triangle?**

DIFFERENTIATION: Supporting the Range of Learners

Intervention Students who need to begin by finding the area of simpler polygons should be encouraged to first build and find the area of a rectangle on their Geoboards, and then move on to a right triangle or a parallelogram. It may help some students to clearly see a square unit if they put rubber bands around each square on the Geoboard and make their shapes with a different colored rubber band.

Extension Students who finish quickly may build more complex shapes on their Geoboards and determine the area.

15 MIN **CLASS**

(3) DISCUSSION

Crazy Cakes

Math Focus Points for Discussion

◆ Dividing irregular polygons into two shapes that have equal area

Display Crazy Cake #6 (T52) on the overhead. Ask students to come to the overhead and explain their solution. As students are sharing their solutions, ask questions such as:

Who has questions for [Cheyenne]? . . . Who can restate what [Cheyenne] did? . . . Does everyone agree that the Crazy Cake is divided equally? Would each person get the same amount of cake?

There are two basic strategies students use to divide the crazy cakes, although sometimes the strategies are combined.

The first is decomposing and comparing shapes. A possible student solution might include dividing the shape into smaller shapes, and showing how these small pieces have equal area.

Students might say:

"I drew a line down the middle. Then I made a rectangle out of the middle six squares—so each side has three square units. The right side has two more squares and one triangle, so that's a total of $5\frac{1}{2}$ square units altogether. The other side has five triangles, so that's $2\frac{1}{2}$ units, plus the three squares. So they're equal!"

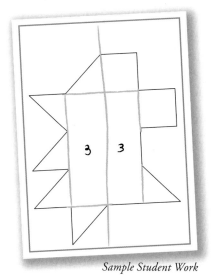

Sample Student Work

Size, Shape, and Symmetry

Crazy Cake #6

T52

▲ **Transparencies, T52**

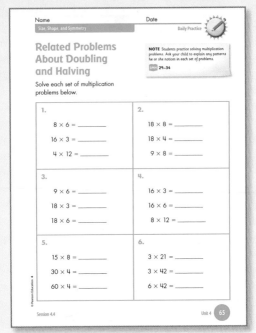

▲ **Student Activity Book, p. 65**

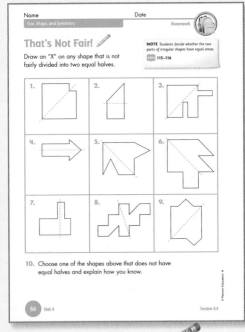

▲ **Student Activity Book, p. 66**

Students use the idea of congruence in this strategy—if pieces are the same size, they have the same area. Some students also create some unit of area (often by creating a grid on the shapes) and count.

The second strategy is *using symmetry.* Some crazy cakes, like Crazy Cake Problem 1, have lines of symmetry and can be divided in half that way. On other crazy cakes, such as Problems 2, 5, and 6, students can decompose and reconfigure the shape to create a symmetrical shape.

Students might say:

 "I moved triangle one to the top, and triangle two up, and that made the shape symmetrical. So the line cuts it equally in half."

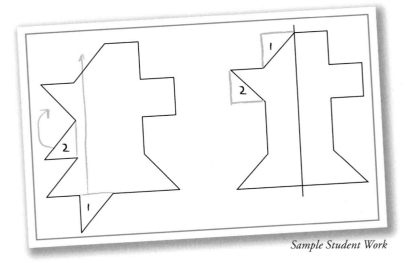

Sample Student Work

SESSION FOLLOW-UP
4 Daily Practice and Homework

Daily Practice: For ongoing review, have students complete *Student Activity Book* page 65.

Homework: On *Student Activity Book* page 66, students look at Crazy Cakes that have been divided and decide whether the two parts have equal area.

Student Math Handbook: Students and families may use *Student Math Handbook* pages 114–115 for reference and review. See pages 170–174 in the back of this unit.

Area of Rectangles

Math Focus Points

◆ Finding the area of polygons using square units

◆ Finding the area of rectangles

◆ Finding the area of triangles in relation to the area of rectangles

Today's Plan		Materials
DISCUSSION **① Area on the Geoboard**	🕙 10 MIN 👥 CLASS	• *Student Activity Book,* p. 63 (from Session 4.4) • T51 (from Session 4.4; optional) • Overhead Geoboard (optional); rubber bands
ACTIVITY **② Introducing Area of Rectangles**	🕔 5 MIN 👥 CLASS	• *Student Activity Book,* pp. 67–68
MATH WORKSHOP **③ Finding Area** **3A** *LogoPaths* Activity: *Mazes* (optional) **3B** Measuring Area on Geoboards **3C** Area of Rectangles	🕙 35 MIN	**3A** • Computers with *LogoPaths* software installed* **3B** • *Student Activity Book,* p. 64 (from Session 4.4) • Geoboards; rubber bands **3C** • *Student Activity Book,* pp. 67–68 (from Activity 2)
DISCUSSION **④ Area of Triangles**	🕙 10 MIN 👥 CLASS	• *Student Activity Book,* p. 64 (completed; from Activity 3B)
SESSION FOLLOW-UP **⑤ Daily Practice**		• *Student Activity Book,* p. 69 • *Student Math Handbook,* pp. 114–115

*See *Materials to Prepare,* p. 111.

Ten-Minute Math

Today's Number: Broken Calculator Students create five expressions that equal 579.
They must use only addition in their expressions. The 5, 7, and 9 keys are broken. Have
two or three students share their equations and explain how they know that the
answer is correct. (Examples: $446 + 133 = 579$ or $448 + 131 = 579$)

Area on the Geoboard

Math Focus Points for Discussion

◆ Finding the area of polygons using square units

Make Shape #2 from *Student Activity Book* page 63 on an overhead Geoboard or draw it on Geoboard Dot Paper (T51).

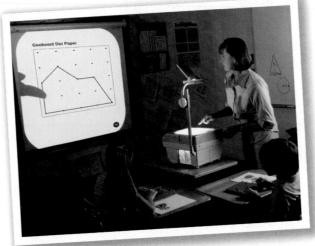

Students find the area of different polygons using square units.

Give students a few minutes to share with a partner how they found the area of the hexagon.

We could break this hexagon into a variety of different smaller pieces to find the area. Who is willing to explain how they found the total area?

Call on a few students to explain their reasoning. Keep stressing that it does not matter how the shape is decomposed; if the area of the smaller shapes is counted correctly and combined, it will always equal the area of the hexagon. Focus on an explanation that includes using a rectangle to find the area of the triangle.

Students might say:

"I divided the shape into three pieces. First, I made a 2 by 3 rectangle, so that's 6 square units. There's two small triangles and so that's another square unit. I made a rectangle around the larger triangle—that rectangle had an area of 2, so the triangle is 1 square unit. So it's 8 square units altogether."❶

Teaching Note

❶ **Area on the Geoboards** If no student brings up this solution, do so yourself.

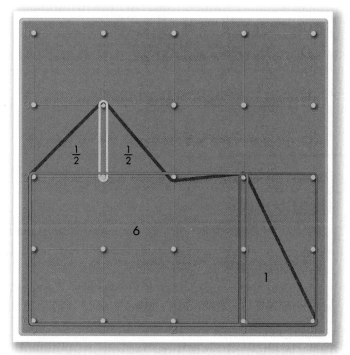

Who can restate how [Jake] found the area of the larger triangle? Did anyone else use a rectangle to find the area of the triangle?

Collect students' ideas about how to use a rectangle to find the area of a right triangle, which could include imagining or drawing the rectangle that the triangle is half of, as Jake did in the example above, or using two copies of the same right triangle to construct a rectangle. Suggest that students continue to think about how rectangles can help them find the area of triangles as they work on the next activity, which they will come back and discuss at the end of the session.

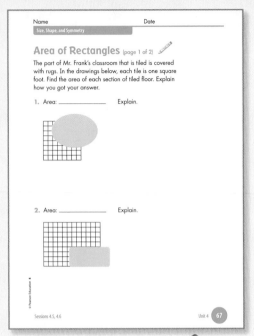

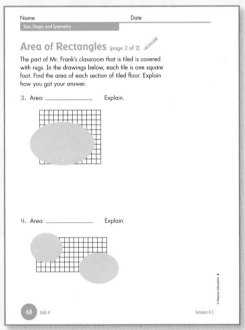

ACTIVITY

5 MIN   CLASS

2 Introducing Area of Rectangles

Direct students' attention to *Student Activity Book* pages 67–68.

There's a new activity in our Math Workshop today. You see in your *Student Activity Book* a rectangle that has been partially covered. Your task is to figure out the area of the whole rectangle. Who has ideas about how you could figure that out?

Accept any student responses. These problems are similar to those students encountered earlier in their array work. If no student brings that up, do so yourself, connecting how they found the product of arrays (using the number of rows and columns and multiplying or skip counting) to finding the area of rectangles.

MATH WORKSHOP

35 MIN

3 Finding Area

Students continue focusing on area, by working on Geoboards and finding the area of rectangles where the entire rectangle cannot be seen. In the *LogoPaths* activity *Mazes,* students finish levels 1–3. If they have already done so, they move on to levels 4 and 5. The discussion at the end of this session focuses on #4 from *Student Activity Book* page 64.

3A *LogoPaths* Activity: *Mazes* (optional)

PAIRS   INDIVIDUALS

For a full description of this activity, see Session 4.3, page 126.

3B Measuring Area on Geoboards

INDIVIDUALS

For a full description of this activity, see Session 4.4, page 132. Students complete *Student Activity Book* page 64.

3C Area of Rectangles

INDIVIDUALS

Students continue finding the area of partially covered rectangles on *Student Activity Book* pages 67–68. Tell students that the solution to Problem 1 will be discussed at the beginning of the next session.

ONGOING ASSESSMENT: Observing Students at Work

Students find the area of rectangles that are partially covered.

- **How do students determine area?** Do they draw gridlines and count squares one-by-one? Do they skip count by rows or columns? Or do they multiply the dimensions of the rectangle?

DISCUSSION

4 **Area of Triangles**

10 MIN **CLASS**

Math Focus Points for Discussion

◆ Finding the area of triangles in relation to the area of rectangles

Make Shape 4 from *Student Activity Book* page 64 on an overhead Geoboard or on Geoboard Dot Paper (T51).

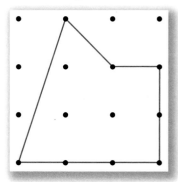

Everyone knew how to find the area of some parts of this pentagon. Everyone found the four whole squares, and knew that the triangle at the top was a half square unit. The part that seemed confusing was this triangle on the left side of the pentagon. Share with a partner how you found the area of this triangle.

Give students a few minutes to do this.

Who wants to explain what they think the area of the triangle is?

At least one student should make a rectangle around the triangle.

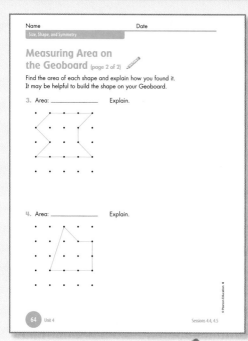

▲ **Student Activity Book, p. 64** WRITING

▲ **Student Activity Book, p. 69**

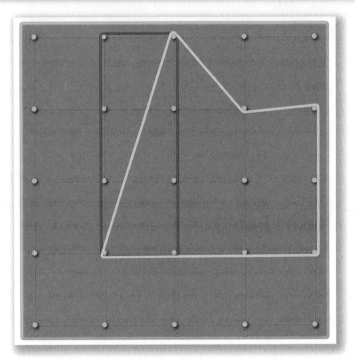

What is the area of the rectangle? . . . How does knowing the area of this rectangle help us determine the area of the triangle?

Students should be able to explain that if the area of the rectangle is three square units, the area of the triangle is $1\frac{1}{2}$ square units. (The diagonal line cuts the rectangle in half, making two congruent triangles.)

SESSION FOLLOW-UP
5 Daily Practice

 Daily Practice: For reinforcement of this unit's content, have students complete *Student Activity Book* page 69.

 Student Math Handbook: Students and families may use *Student Math Handbook* pages 114–115 for reference and review. See pages 170–174 in the back of this unit.

Area of Polygons

Math Focus Points

◆ Finding the area of rectangles

◆ Finding the area of polygons by decomposing shapes

Today's Plan		Materials
① DISCUSSION **Area of Rectangles**	10 MIN CLASS	• *Student Activity Book,* p. 67 (from Session 4.5)
② ACTIVITY **Area of Polygons**	35 MIN INDIVIDUALS	• *Student Activity Book,* pp. 70–72
③ DISCUSSION **Decomposing Shapes**	15 MIN CLASS	• *Student Activity Book,* pp. 70–72 (from Activity 2)
④ SESSION FOLLOW-UP **Daily Practice and Homework**		• *Student Activity Book,* pp. 73–74 • *Student Math Handbook,* pp. 114–115

Ten-Minute Math

Today's Number: Broken Calculator Students create five expressions that equal 1,115. They must use only subtraction in their expressions. The 1 and 5 keys are broken. Have two or three students share their equations and explain how they know that the answer is correct. (Examples: 3,437 — 2,322 = 1,115 or 4,437 — 3,322 = 1,115)

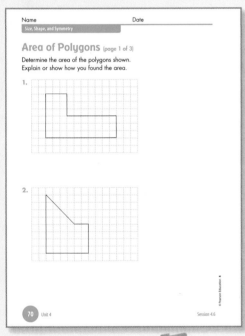

▲ Student Activity Book, p. 70

10 MIN   CLASS

DISCUSSION
① Area of Rectangles

Math Focus Points for Discussion

◆ Finding the area of rectangles

Ask students to share with their neighbor the answer they found for Problem 1 on Student Activity Book page 67. Then ask for volunteers to explain their solution to the entire class. For each explanation, ask questions such as:

Who has questions for [Derek]? Who solved the problem the same way? Who did it a different way?

Students might say:

"I drew the lines over the rug so I could see the whole array. It was 8 by 8, and I know that's 64."

"I looked at the bottom two rows. There's eight in a row, and two rows, so that's 16. So then I counted two rows at a time, so it was 16, 32, 48, 64."

"I could see that the dimensions of the floor were 8 by 8, so I multiplied and got 64."

If time remains, discuss solutions to other problems.

35 MIN   INDIVIDUALS

ACTIVITY
② Area of Polygons

For our last activity about area, you're going to find the area of different polygons. Since none of them are rectangles, you're going to use what you know about decomposing shapes and finding the area of rectangles to solve these problems. Using symmetry might also be helpful.

Students complete *Student Activity Book* pages 70–72. Problems 3 and 4 are discussed at the end of the session.❶

As you circulate and observe students, ask questions such as:

- Do you see smaller shapes within the entire shape that you can find the area of?

- How did you find the area of the triangles?

- Is there a rectangle you could make around the triangle that helps you figure that out?

- Are any of these shapes symmetrical? What does that tell you about the area of the shape?

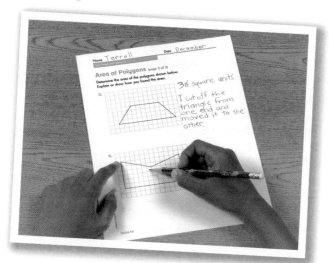

Students find the area of non-rectangular shapes.

ONGOING ASSESSMENT: Observing Students at Work

Students find the area of polygons by decomposing shapes.

- **How do students decompose shapes?** Are they keeping track of each "piece" to find the total of the whole polygon?

- **How are students finding the area of rectangles?** Are they counting individual squares? Skip counting? Using the dimensions and multiplying?

- **How are students finding the area of triangles?** In Problem 2, are they counting each as $\frac{1}{2}$ square unit? Are they making rectangles around the triangles in Problems 2 to 5? Do they understand why making the rectangle gives them the area of the triangle?

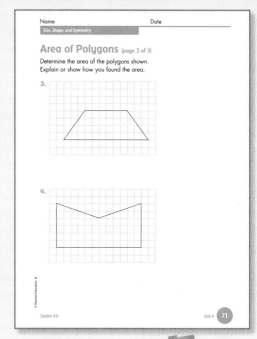

▲ **Student Activity Book, p. 71**

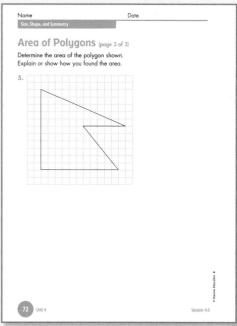

▲ **Student Activity Book, p. 72**

DIFFERENTIATION: Supporting the Range of Learners

Intervention Students who are still working with the idea of the area of triangles should solve Problems 1 and 2. (Because the triangle in section 2 has $\frac{1}{2}$ square units, they should be able to count those.) For Problems 3–5, have these students draw lines to make the polygon into a rectangle, and have them find the area of this new rectangle (e.g., #3 becomes a 12 by 4 rectangle, #4 becomes 12 by 6, and #5 becomes 11 by 11).

DISCUSSION
3 Decomposing Shapes

15 MIN CLASS

Math Focus Points for Discussion

◆ Finding the area of polygons by decomposing shapes

Ask students to explain their solutions to Problems 3 and 4 on *Student Activity Book* page 71, and then ask such questions as the following:

Who has questions for [Lucy]? . . . Who can restate what [Lucy] did? . . . Who else used a similar strategy? . . . Does everyone agree with the answer?

Possible student strategies for Problem 3 include:

- Decomposing the shape into a rectangle and triangles: "I made a 6×4 rectangle so that's 24 square units. Both triangles are the same size. I put a rectangle around one of them and the rectangle was 3 by 4, so the triangle is 6 square units. Since there's two, I doubled it so it's 12 square units. $24 + 12 = 36$ square units."

- Decomposing and reconfiguring the shape: "Since the two triangles are the same, I moved one, and turned it so it made a rectangle with the other one. That made a 9 by 4 rectangle, so it's 36 square units."

Possible student strategies for Problem #4 include similar strategies as #3 (a 12 by 4 rectangle, two triangles that have an area of six square units; or moving one of the triangles on top of the other one, so that the shape could be reconfigured to a 12 by 4 rectangle and a 2 by 6 rectangle.) Another strategy that students might use is this:

- Using symmetry to find the area of $\frac{1}{2}$ the shape, then doubling the amount to find the area of the whole shape: "I noticed the shape was symmetrical, so I drew a line down the middle of it. That made a 6 by 4 rectangle which is 24 square units. The triangle at the top is six units, so that's 30 square units. So that makes the area of the whole shape 60 square units." (This strategy also works for Problem 3, but the symmetry is less obvious.)

SESSION FOLLOW-UP
Daily Practice and Homework

 Daily Practice: For reinforcement of this unit's content, have students complete *Student Activity Book* page 73.

 Homework: Students use area measurement to determine which is the larger of two rectangles in a pair on *Student Activity Book* page 74.

 Student Math Handbook: Students and families may use *Student Math Handbook* pages 114–115 for reference and review. See pages 170–174 in the back of this unit.

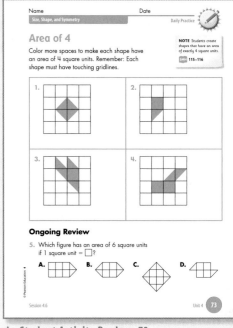

▲ Student Activity Book, p. 73

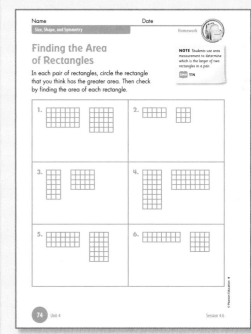

▲ Student Activity Book, p. 74

End-of-Unit Assessment

Math Focus Points

◆ Recognizing number of sides as a descriptor of various polygons

◆ Identifying a right angle as 90 degrees

◆ Measuring acute angles by relating them to 90 degrees

◆ Finding the area of polygons by decomposing shapes

Today's Plan		Materials
ASSESSMENT ACTIVITY **① End-of-Unit Assessment**	✓ ◷ ☻ 60 MIN INDIVIDUALS	• M27–M28* • Power Polygon Piece L
SESSION FOLLOW-UP **② Daily Practice**		• *Student Activity Book,* p. 75 • *Student Math Handbook,* pp. 107–116

*See *Materials to Prepare,* p. 111.

Ten-Minute Math

Today's Number: Broken Calculator Students create five expressions that equal 641. They must use only addition in their expressions. The 1, 4, and 6 keys are broken. Have two or three students share their equations and explain how they know that the answer is correct. (Examples: 299 + 270 + 72 = 641 or 299 + 250 + 92 = 641)

ASSESSMENT ACTIVITY

1 End-of-Unit Assessment

60 MIN INDIVIDUALS

On End-of-Unit Assessment (M27–M28), students work individually to solve two problems designed to assess three of the unit's benchmarks.❶❷

The first problem assesses Benchmarks 2 and 3. Students compose shapes from other shapes with certain angle measures. Benchmark 4 is assessed in Problem 2 as students find the area of a shape.

Students who finish this assessment before the end of the session may work on the computer *LogoPaths* activities or return to any unfinished Math Workshop activities.

ONGOING ASSESSMENT: Observing Students at Work

Students build and identify polygons that include quadrilaterals, identify angle sizes, and find the area of a quadrilateral in square units.

- **Do students make and correctly identify at least two different 4-sided figures as quadrilaterals?**

- **Do students correctly identify a right angle as 90 degrees?** Correctly identify a 60-degree angle? Do they correctly identify an angle that is greater than 90 degrees?

- **Do students correctly find the area of the quadrilateral in square units, either by decomposing and reconfiguring the shape to make square units, counting square units and square unit equivalents, and/or using symmetry?**

- **Do students know that a small right triangle is half of a square unit?**

- **Do students demonstrate understanding that two right triangles can be combined to make a rectangle, and therefore the area of the right triangle is half the area of the corresponding rectangle?**

Teaching Note

❶ **Reviewing the Directions** The directions for Problem 1 include a number of things that students must pay attention to as they construct polygons with Power Polygon piece L. In order to ensure that students do not leave out one or more of these directions, you may want to spend a few minutes at the beginning of the session going over the directions with the class, and clarifying any questions they may have.

Professional Development

❷ **Teacher Note:** End-of-Unit Assessment, p. 159

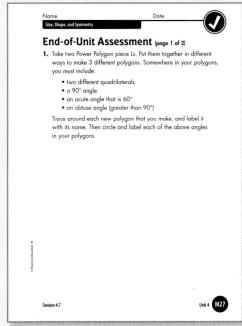

Name _____ Date _____
Size, Shape, and Symmetry

End-of-Unit Assessment (page 1 of 2)

1. Take two Power Polygon piece Ls. Put them together in different ways to make 3 different polygons. Somewhere in your polygons, you must include:
   - two different quadrilaterals
   - a 90° angle
   - an acute angle that is 60°
   - an obtuse angle (greater than 90°)

Trace around each new polygon that you make, and label it with its name. Then circle and label each of the above angles in your polygons.

Session 4.7   Unit 4 M27

▲ **Resource Masters, M27**

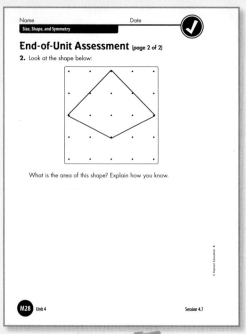

Name _____ Date _____

Size, Shape, and Symmetry

End-of-Unit Assessment (page 2 of 2)

2. Look at the shape below:

What is the area of this shape? Explain how you know.

M28 Unit 4   Session 4.7

▲ **Resource Masters, M28** PORTFOLIO

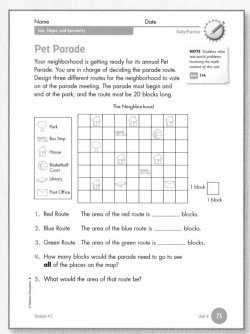

Name _____ Date _____

Size, Shape, and Symmetry   Daily Practice

Pet Parade

Your neighborhood is getting ready for its annual Pet
Parade. You are in charge of deciding the parade route.
Design three different routes for the neighborhood to vote
on at the parade meeting. The parade must begin and
end at the park, and the route must be 20 blocks long.

NOTE Students solve
real-world problems
involving the math
content of this unit.
Step 114

The Neighborhood

Park
Bus Stop
House
Basketball Court
Library
Post Office

1 block
1 block

1. Red Route   The area of the red route is _____ blocks.

2. Blue Route   The area of the blue route is _____ blocks.

3. Green Route   The area of the green route is _____ blocks.

4. How many blocks would the parade need to go to see
   all of the places on the map?

5. What would the area of that route be?

Session 4.7   Unit 4 75

▲ **Student Activity Book, p. 75**

DIFFERENTIATION: Supporting the Range of Learners

Intervention Some students may need help organizing all the
information that is asked for in Problem 1. Have these students check
off each of the bulleted directions to be sure that they have included
them in the polygons they drew.

Intervention Some students may need help articulating their work on
Problem 2. Help these students by having them first explain to you in
words their strategy for finding the area, and then have them write
what they said.

SESSION FOLLOW-UP
2 Daily Practice

Daily Practice: For enrichment, have students complete *Student
Activity Book* page 75.

Student Math Handbook: Students and families may use
Student Math Handbook pages 107–116 for reference and review.
See pages 170–174 in the back of this unit.

Size, Shape, and Symmetry

In Part 6 of *Implementing Investigations in Grade 4,* you will find a set of Teacher Notes that addresses topics and issues applicable to the curriculum as a whole rather than to specific curriculum units. They include the following:

Computational Fluency and Place Value

Computational Algorithms and Methods

Representations and Contexts for Mathematical Work

Foundations of Algebra in the Elementary Grades

Discussing Mathematical Ideas

Racial and Linguistic Diversity in the Classroom:
   What Does Equity Mean in Today's Math Classroom?

Metric and U.S. Standard Measures

Only the United States and two other countries (currently Liberia and Myanmar) are not officially metric. In many countries, people are unfamiliar with the U.S. (or English) standard units that we use. They buy food by the kilogram and drinks by the liter. They drive kilometers per hour in cars powered with gas bought by the liter. They know their height in centimeters, their weight in kilograms, and the temperature in Celsius.

Most countries use the metric system, and the increasingly global marketplace has led experts to predict that the United States will soon convert. It is important for students to become familiar with metric measurement, as well as work with U.S. standard measures including pounds, feet, and miles.

One useful aspect of the metric system is that it is based on powers of 10. This simplifies calculations and conversions. Prefixes are used across measurement types to denote the magnitude, or power of 10, of the measure in question. The most common of these are *kilo-, centi-,* and *milli-. Kilo-* means 1,000, therefore 1,000 meters is a *kilometer. Centi-* means one-hundredth, therefore one-hundredth of a meter is a *centimeter. Milli-* means one-thousandth; a *millimeter* is one-thousandth of a meter. Other metric prefixes, such as *deca-, deci-,* and *hecta-,* are less commonly used.

Adults who are accustomed to U.S. standard measure may use them as benchmarks to get a sense of metric units. For example, you probably know that a meter is a little longer than a yard and that a kilometer is a little longer than half a mile.

In this unit, students learn about linear metric measures through their own experiences as they compare them to objects. Thus, they might learn:

A millimeter is about the thickness of a dime or a paper clip wire.

A centimeter is about the width of a paper clip.

A meter is about the length from the tip of your fingers to your opposite shoulder.

The height of a tall man is about 200 centimeters.

Students practice measuring real-world objects using the metric system.

Introducing Benchmarks

A benchmark is something familiar that is about the same size as a particular unit of measurement. We can use benchmarks to help estimate the size of something when a measuring tool is not handy. For example, if we know that the nail of our index finger is about a centimeter wide, we can use it to estimate length in centimeters. We can also use benchmarks to help us understand and remember the size of a measurement unit.

When introducing benchmarks to the class, encourage students to share ways that measurement units have become meaningful to them. In one class, the teacher began by telling a story about a benchmark of her own:

"When I was a little girl, I lived in a house that was at the top of a hill. My mother was a wonderful cook. She loved to bake. A lot of times, she'd be in the middle of baking and she'd run out of an ingredient. She used to send me to the store for five-pound bags of sugar or flour. If I think back to walking up that hill with that bag, I have a memory of what five pounds feels like. So now whenever somebody tells me that something weighs about five pounds, I remember what it felt like to carry those five-pound bags of sugar up that hill."

After the teacher told her story, she invited students to share stories about familiar benchmarks. Several students shared ways that they found meaning for a mile:

Alejandro: When you walk a mile, it takes about half an hour. When my mom and I run together on Saturdays, we go four times around the track to make a mile. I don't know how long it takes, but I get really tired!

Amelia: I like watching the odometer in the car when my parents drive. Sometimes I time how long it takes to go a mile. It takes about a minute when we're on the highway, but sometimes when we're in traffic it takes a minute and a half, or two minutes, or even longer.

Cheyenne: It's a mile to downtown from school. I know because I bike downtown to my flute lesson after school every Thursday.

Bill: I used to live in New York City, and there a wide city block is about a tenth of a mile, so when you walk ten blocks across town, you go a mile. And when you walk on the short ends of the blocks it takes twenty blocks to go a mile.

The more that students can bring their out-of-school experiences into math class, the more meaningful and engaging learning will be. As students share the ways that they have come to develop benchmarks, they develop new insights about the meaning of measurement units.

Introducing and Managing *LogoPaths*

LogoPaths software is provided as a component of the *Investigations* curriculum. While the use of this software is optional, we recommend its use if you have computers available. In this unit, *LogoPaths* games and activities are introduced in each investigation and then integrated into the Math Workshop activities. The software activities extend and deepen the mathematical ideas that are emphasized in this unit and in some cases the software activities allow students to do work with geometric figures and work with angles in ways that they are not able to in the off-computer activities.

In this unit, activities with the *LogoPaths* software are suggested throughout each Investigation. How you introduce and incorporate these computer activities into your curriculum depends on the number of computers and level of technology available.

First you will need to consider how you will introduce your students to the *LogoPaths* software. Then you will need to consider how students will have access to the software. If you have access to a large screen and a projector, you can introduce each new software activity to the whole class. If you have access to a computer lab, consider introducing each new activity to the whole class in this environment. If your school has a computer teacher, you might collaborate with that teacher to have students work on these activities during some of their scheduled time in the computer lab. In this unit the activities are included as Math Workshop activities so once students are introduced to an activity they can then access the activity during Math Workshops.

Regardless of the number of computers you have, students generally benefit by working on these activities in pairs. This not only maximizes computer resources, but also encourages students to consult, monitor, and teach one another. Generally, more than two students at one computer find it difficult to share. You may need to monitor computer use closely to ensure that all students get sufficient computer time. Each pair should spend at least 15–20 minutes at the computer for each activity.

Options for Introducing the *LogoPaths* Software

Computer Lab If you have a computer laboratory with one computer for each pair of students, all of your students can be introduced to and can become familiar with the computer activities at the same time. In this situation you will not need to devote time during math class for introducing students to the new software activity. Students will access the activity during Math Workshop.

Large Screen Monitor or Projection Screen If you have access to either of these devices you can introduce the software activities to the whole class during the math session immediately before Math Workshop or at another time of the day.

Small Groups of Students You can introduce the software activities to small groups of students either before or during Math Workshop. These students can then be paired with other students and become "teachers" of the software.

Managing the Computer Environment

Math Workshop Students should have access to the *LogoPaths* software consistently throughout the unit. If you have daily access to a computer lab, you might choose to add this experience into your day in addition to your regular math class. A more typical situation is that classrooms have a small number of computers in the classroom. While three to five computers is ideal, students can have a successful computer experience with only one to two computers. In the case that there are fewer computers, you will need to incorporate additional computer time for students throughout the day. If you have computers available in your classroom, pairs of students can cycle through the computer activities, just as they cycle through the other Math Workshop activities.

Using *LogoPaths* All Year This is the only unit in the Grade 4 sequence that explicitly suggests computer activities to go with specific sessions of the unit. However, along with the suggested activities in units prior to this one, suggestions and Teacher Resources are included in later units for activities that students can continue for the remainder of the school year. Continued experience with *LogoPaths* allows them to become increasingly fluent in the mechanics of the software and able to better focus on the mathematical ideas of the games and activities. Students should continue to explore the games that develop understanding of paths and turning angles and the *Free Explore* activities that focus on the properties of 2-D shapes, including their angles. Students will build on their knowledge and experiences with the *LogoPaths* software in Grade 5.

Introducing the *LogoPaths* Activities

In your first introduction of the *Missing Measures* activity, show students the following:

- How to open *Free Explore* by clicking on it once

- How to enter forward and backward commands of any amount in the Command Center (e.g., **FD 82**, **BK 125**) (Note that move and turn inputs must be between −999 and 999.)

- How to enter right and left turn commands in multiples of 30° (e.g., **RT 90**, **LT 120**)

- How to use the **Label Length** and **Label Turns** tools

- How to use the **HT** (hide turtle) and **ST** (show turtle) commands

In your first introduction of the *600 (800) Steps* activity, show students the following:

- How to open *Free Explore* by clicking on it once

- How to enter forward and backward commands of any amount in the Command Center (e.g., **FD 82**, **BK 125**)

- How to use the **Label Length** and **Label Turns** tools

- How to use the **HT** (hide turtle) and **ST** (show turtle) commands

- How to use the **Teach** tool to make a procedure out of a set of commands and give it a name

In your first introduction of the *Mazes* game, show students the following:

- How to open *Mazes* by clicking on it once

- How to select the level they wish to play

- How to enter right and left turn commands with any number of degrees as input (e.g., **RT 50**, **LT 114**)

- How to use the **Turtle Turner** and the **Ruler** tool

You can introduce more of the tools available in *LogoPaths* as students indicate interest and the need to use them.

Students can use the penup (**PU**) and pendown (**PD**) commands to have the turtle draw or not draw as it moves. Type **PU** in the Command Center to move without drawing. Type **PD** for the turtle to draw as it moves.

The repeat command tells the turtle to repeat a set of commands a specified number of times. The first input is the number of times to repeat, and the second is a list of commands enclosed in square brackets. For example, to repeat a forward move and a right turn four times, students might type **REPEAT 4 [FD 100 RT 90]**, which would in this case result in a square with sides lengths 100 turtle steps long.

Students can change the color, shape and size of the turtle and the line it draws using the Turtle Preferences panel. Other features of how the turtle works (e.g., its speed) can be changed in the Preferences panel.

Further information about commands, tools and buttons can be found in the online Help.

It is likely that many students will discover other tools and their uses on their own as they spend more time working with the software. Encourage them to share their discoveries with one another.

Saving Student Work

If you want to discuss students' work later, they should either print it or save their work on disks. For information about printing or saving to a disk, see the *Software Support Resource Guide* contained on the software CD.

Teacher Note

About the Mathematics in the *LogoPaths* Software

The *LogoPaths* software provides an environment in which students can explore ideas of geometry, patterns, logical thinking, and more. The essential metaphor in Logo is "playing turtle"—taking the perspective of the turtle (the drawing cursor) to move and turn to make shapes and designs. This is a very natural view of geometry for children because it matches how we make our way through the world by asking, "How much further do I need to move? Which way should I turn to get to a particular place?" Standing outside the situation to view it like a map is more difficult.

Students explore a number of geometric and other mathematical ideas when they use *LogoPaths*. This includes explicit investigation of length and perimeter and ideas such as the equality of lengths of opposite sides in a parallelogram. It also includes exploration of the sizes of angles, and the relationship between the turning (or exterior) angle and the interior angle of polygons. *LogoPaths* is another context in which students come to see a variety of representations of numerical ideas—bigger or smaller means a different thing with length, angle, number of sides, etc.

Using the *LogoPaths* software in Grades 3 through 5 also allows students to explore many kinds of patterns and relationships. For example, they discover that the first two sides of a rectangle always have half the total perimeter; that consecutive sides of a parallelogram have turning angles that sum to 180°; that a polygon with only 90-degree turns always has an even number of sides; or that the turning (exterior) angles in a polygon sum to 360 degrees (which means the turning angle in a regular polygon is always 360 divided by the number of sides). You can encourage students to look for a wide variety of patterns and see if they can explain when they are true and why they might always be true. Creating procedures with variable inputs is another

way of focusing on regularities and patterns—such procedures define a whole class of shapes with the same structure, but different sizes, or with different angles, etc.

LogoPaths offers students a chance to *see* a variety of inverse operations—that is, pairs of commands that undo each others' effects. For example, moving forward and then back the same amount leaves the turtle in the same place. Other inverse operations include right and left, penup and pendown, and hide turtle and show turtle. Students can also explore arithmetic inverses, with addition and subtraction, multiplication and division, or with positive and negative numbers. The idea of an inverse is very important mathematically, and *LogoPaths* helps students visualize this idea.

Students learn careful logical thinking by working with *LogoPaths*. Because the turtle only does exactly what students tell it to do, no more and no less, they learn to be precise in their instructions. And if the turtle does something unexpected, students learn to break the instructions down step by step by "playing turtle" to figure out just how their instructions led to this unexpected behavior and, therefore, how to change them. Some of *LogoPaths'* debugging tools (e.g., the Stop tool, the Step tool and highlighting of steps, even through procedures in the Teach window) can help in this process. (The *Software Support Reference Guide* and the online Help text provide more information about these tools.) By making procedures that can be used by other procedures, students also break down complex ideas and projects into smaller, more manageable chunks. For example, a procedure to make a house might move the turtle to the right positions and then use a square procedure for windows, a rectangle procedure for the door, and a triangle procedure for the roof. These sorts of logical and analytical problem-solving approaches are important to mathematical thinking.

Teacher Note

Beyond Vocabulary

The work in this unit may introduce new vocabulary to students. As students work together to construct polygons and angles from the Power Polygons, and as they describe the characteristics of triangles, quadrilaterals, and angles, you will hear them talk about the shapes using their own words. For example, a *pointy angle* might mean an acute angle (less than 90 degrees), and a *wide angle* might be an obtuse one (greater than 90 degrees). The activities in this unit, however, will provide opportunities for students to use more precise language.

As students work to make themselves clear, you might hear some unusual, but accurate, descriptions. For example, one student described angles this way: "An angle is two lines attached by the ends. They're either pulling away from each other or pushing to get closer. The shape they make while doing that is the angle."

Although mathematically, the "lines" in the student's description are actually rays (meaning that they continue on indefinitely), the student does understand that an angle is formed by two sides and a vertex. She also has a sense of the motion of turning that defines the size of the angle, which she visualizes as "pulling away" or "pushing closer." At this point, having such a visual image will serve her far better than being given a more mathematically correct definition of "angle." For all students, it is important to achieve a balance between using technical vocabulary and the less formal terms that make sense to students as they explore geometric objects.

Students will learn the mathematical terms as they hear them in context. Use the correct terms and informally explain to students what they mean. As students hear you and others use the terms, they will adopt the ones that make sense to them—but this process will take time. Do not expect students to use terms the first few times they hear them. The activities in this unit provide repeated experience with the same terms and concepts, so students will have a number of opportunities to pick up new vocabulary. Be aware that some students will adopt it easily, while others will need more time. It is not expected that all fourth graders will be fluent with the use of geometric vocabulary by the end of this unit.

Avoid the temptation to stop and teach a lesson specifically on vocabulary or to test students on vocabulary words. More important is that students develop accurate concepts for the shapes for which they already have names. Many fourth graders (and even older students) have limited ideas about even familiar shapes. For example, they may believe that a triangle must have two equal sides, or that squares that are tilted may not be squares at all. Help students build concepts without expecting definitions to be clarifying. Allow them to try out their ideas in class discussions, but expect them to make themselves clear and to justify their conjectures.

Teacher Note

Classification of Quadrilaterals

Classification systems help us organize the world into categories that are often hierarchical and overlapping. For example, a person might live in the city of Cleveland, which is in the state of Ohio, which is in the United States, which is in North America. If you know someone who lives in Cleveland, you also know that that person lives in Ohio, and in the United States, and in North America.

Mathematicians use a hierarchical classification system to sort geometric figures. In this unit, students consider this as it applies to what they know about the general category of shapes that have four sides, called quadrilaterals. Quadrilaterals are classified by looking at their sides and their angles. When sides are being considered, the characteristics to pay attention to are the length of the sides and whether or not pairs of sides are parallel. For example, *trapezoids* have exactly one pair of parallel sides that are not equal in length, and opposite nonparallel sides that may or may not be equal in length. If one pair of opposite sides in a trapezoid is equal in length, this is called an *isosceles trapezoid,* which is the trapezoid that fourth graders are most familiar with. A trapezoid can also be further classified by whether it contains a right angle.

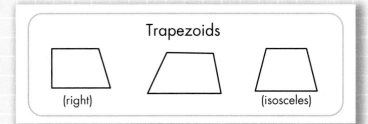

Trapezoids

(right)   (isosceles)

Parallelograms have two pairs of parallel sides, and opposite sides are equal in length. *Rhombuses* (or rhombi) are members of the parallelogram family that have all four sides equal. Rectangles are also members of the parallelogram family. The angles are what make rectangles special; all four angles are equal, and measure 90 degrees. Squares, then, are in many families, including rectangle (because the angles are all the same size), rhombus (because the sides are all the same

length), and parallelogram (because there are two pairs of parallel sides).

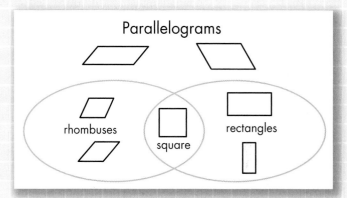

Parallelograms

rhombuses   square   rectangles

Other kinds of quadrilaterals do not fit into the categories of either trapezoids or parallelograms, because they do not have any parallel sides. These quadrilaterals may, however, have some sides that are equal in length, such as the first two examples in the figure below. Quadrilaterals may have angles that are four different sizes, as in the second two examples below. They may also have an angle that is greater than 180 degrees which makes a *concave* quadrilateral, as in the last two examples.

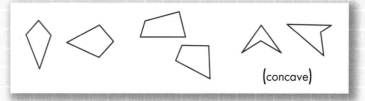

(concave)

Such traditional classifications are just one useful way to sort geometric figures. One could just as well declare that rectangles *cannot* have all equal sides, and then squares would not be in the family of rectangles. Students often initially prefer this partitioning way of classifying. Only with time will they come to see the advantages of hierarchical classification— for example, if you know that a square is a rectangle, you then know that it has all the properties of rectangles.

At this age, students will benefit from thinking and communicating about the properties of polygons, but they need not have the whole classification system in mind.

Assessment: What Is a Quadrilateral?

Benchmark addressed:

Benchmark 2: Identify quadrilaterals as any four-sided closed figure.

In order to meet the benchmark, students' work should show that they can:

- Demonstrate understanding that a quadrilateral must have four sides, but can have a variety of side lengths and angle sizes;

- Identify shapes that are quadrilaterals as well as shapes that are not;

- Include shapes other than squares and rectangles.

It is likely that many students will use squares and rectangles as examples of quadrilaterals. However, in order to meet the benchmark, their definitions must somehow be inclusive of other quadrilaterals, such as those with nonright angles. For example, their definitions might simply say that quadrilaterals have four sides and four angles—in this case they meet the benchmark. However, if some students' definitions specify that quadrilaterals must have right angles or sides of equal length, they only partially meet the benchmark, because they are limiting their definitions to only some quadrilaterals.

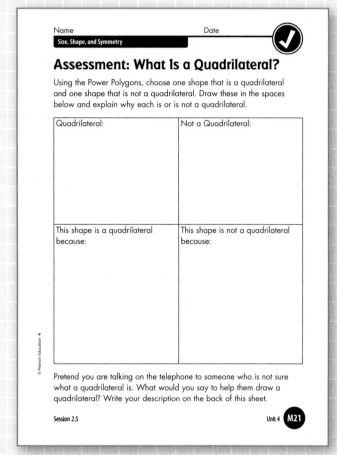

▲ **Resource Masters, M21**

Meeting the Benchmark

Alejandro drew a square as his example of a quadrilateral. He wrote that a quadrilateral is "any type of polygon with four sides."

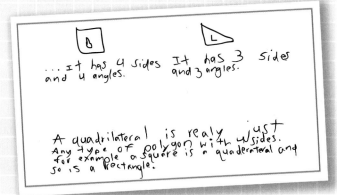

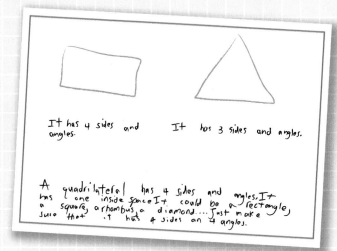

Alejandro's Work

Cheyenne drew a rectangle as her example of a quadrilateral. Her description also includes a rhombus and what she calls a "diamond" (by which she may mean a quadrilateral that is oriented on one angle rather than a side).

Cheyenne's Work

Anna drew a trapezoid as her example of a quadrilateral, and wrote that "all the sides don't have to be the same length."

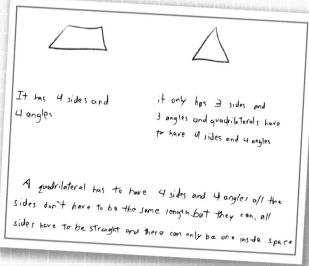

Anna's Work

Partially Meeting the Benchmark

Bill drew a rectangle as his example of a quadrilateral. His definition, however, limits the size of the angles to right angles.

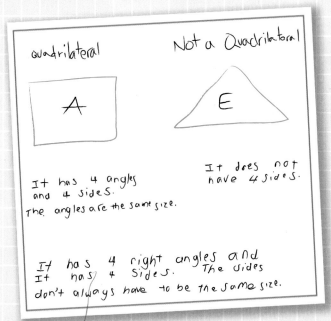

Bill's Work

Amelia also drew a rectangle (which she may possibly have intended as a square, since it is drawn freehand), and then wrote that quadrilaterals must have "equal sides."

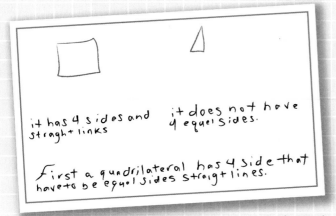

Amelia's Work

When student responses only include squares or rectangles as quadrilaterals, question them to determine whether they understand that nonrectangular four-sided figures are also quadrilaterals. Choose one or two of the Power Polygons, such as shape G (rhombus) or shape K (trapezoid) and ask

whether these shapes could be quadrilaterals also. You may find that some students do include these in their definitions, but did not think to write about them. For students who still need to expand their definitions beyond squares and rectangles, show them a variety of quadrilaterals that include nonright angles and ask them what these shapes have in common (four sides). These students may also benefit from spending more time playing *Guess My Rule*.

Not Meeting the Benchmark

Students who either identify a shape other than a four-sided figure as a quadrilateral or draw a nonrectangular quadrilateral as an example of a shape that is not a quadrilateral, do not meet the benchmark. These students will need to spend more time constructing and identifying four-sided figures with a variety of side lengths and angle sizes. You may want to provide straws or toothpicks with clay for connectors to have students make a variety of quadrilaterals, or have students create a poster of quadrilaterals that divides them into subcategories, such as with and without right angles.

End-of-Unit Assessment

Problem 1

Benchmarks addressed:

Benchmark 2: Identify quadrilaterals as any four-sided closed figure.

Benchmark 3: Know that a right angle measures 90 degrees, and use this as a landmark to find angles of 30, 45, and 60 degrees.

In order to meet Benchmark 2, students' work should show that they can:

• Make and correctly identify at least two different four-sided figures as quadrilaterals.

In order to meet Benchmark 3, students' work should show that they can:

• Identify a right angle as 90 degrees;

• Identify a 60-degree angle;

• Identify an angle that is greater than 90 degrees.

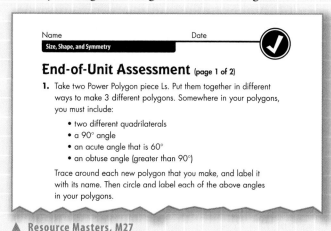

▲ Resource Masters, M27

Students who meet both benchmarks include all of the above in their work. You may find that some students meet only one benchmark or the other for this problem. If that is the case, see the section below about students who partially meet the benchmark for suggestions of how to address

whichever of the two benchmarks these students still need to work on.

Meeting the Benchmarks

The following are examples of students who meet both benchmarks.

Ramona drew a rectangle and a nonrectangular quadrilateral, as well as a triangle for her third polygon. She correctly labeled all three kinds of angles, including the 60-degree angle which is a combination of the two 30-degree angles in Power Polygon piece L.

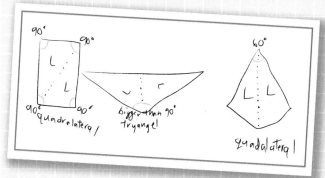

Ramona's Work

Derek drew a rectangle, a parallelogram, and an equilateral triangle. He recognizes that all of the angles in the rectangle are 90 degrees, that all of the angles in the triangle are 60 degrees, and that opposite angles on the parallelogram have the same measure.

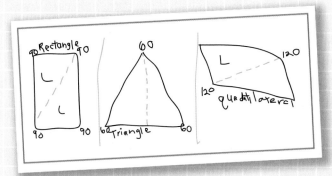

Derek's Work

Ursula drew the same two quadrilaterals as Ramona. For her third polygon, she made a concave pentagon. She identifies 90-degree angles, and accurately identifies one of each of the other angle sizes as well.

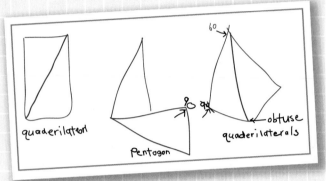

Ursula's Work

Partially Meeting the Benchmarks

Benchmark 2

Some students may correctly draw two different quadrilaterals, but mislabel one of them. For example, they may call a rectangle that sits on its shorter side a square because they visualize rectangles as "long and skinny." Determine whether this was a simple error, and question these students about what they know about the difference between a square and a rectangle. If a student is still very unsure about the distinction, they do not meet the benchmark, and should continue to work on classifying a variety of quadrilaterals, such as by playing *Guess My Rule*.

Benchmark 3

Students who correctly label a 90-degree angle and at least one of the other two angles but not both, only *partially* meet the benchmark. Determine whether this was an error of omission, and ask students to double-check their work. If some students are unsure about one of the angle sizes, they will need more opportunities to measure angles with the Power Polygons, using a 90-degree angle as their reference point.

Not Meeting the Benchmarks

Benchmark 2

Students who can draw only one type of quadrilateral, which is likely to be a rectangle given the shape of Power Polygon piece L, do not meet the benchmark. Some students may draw two rectangles that are oriented differently on the page as their two examples of quadrilaterals. Because it is important that students know that any four-sided figure is a quadrilateral, these students do not meet the benchmark. These students will need to spend more time constructing and identifying four-sided figures with a variety of side lengths and angle sizes. You may want to provide straws or toothpicks with clay for connectors to have students make a variety of quadrilaterals, or have students create a poster of quadrilaterals that divides them into subcategories, such as with and without right angles.

Benchmark 3

Students who cannot identify a right angle will most likely not be able to correctly identify angles of other sizes. Students need to be able to visually recognize the "squareness" of a 90-degree angle, in order to be able to use this as a reference point for comparing and measuring other angles. These students should spend time first looking for right angles in objects around them, using the corner of a piece of paper as a guideline, and then looking for other angles that are both larger and smaller than right angles. Give them opportunities to do the same with shapes on the Shape Cards and the Power Polygons. These students may also benefit from spending more time with the activity *Making Right Angles,* from Investigation 3.

Problem 2

Benchmark addressed:

Benchmark 4: Find the area of polygons using a square unit of measure.

In order to meet the benchmark, students' work should show that they can:

- Correctly find the area of the quadrilateral in square units, either by decomposing and reconfiguring the shape to make square units, counting square units and square unit equivalents, and/or using symmetry;

- Know that a small right triangle is half of a square unit;

- Demonstrate understanding that two larger right triangles can be combined to make a rectangle, and therefore the area of the right triangle is half the area of the corresponding rectangle.

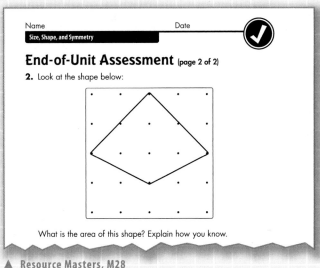

Name _____ Date _____

Size, Shape, and Symmetry

End-of-Unit Assessment (page 2 of 2)

2. Look at the shape below:

What is the area of this shape? Explain how you know.

▲ **Resource Masters, M28**

As you are looking at student work for this problem, consider both what students draw on the Geoboard figure as well as their explanations. It is not unusual for fourth graders to be able to show their thinking clearly with their drawings, but not be able to articulate it as clearly in their writing. As long as students' solutions are correct and it is clear how they came up with those solutions, either in their drawing or their writing, they meet the benchmark.

Meeting the Benchmark

Lucy broke the figure apart into squares and triangles. She appears to be confident in her knowledge that the small right triangle is half of a square and the larger right triangles at the bottom of the figure each equal one square. Her work shows how she added half squares, and how she counted squares and square-equivalents.

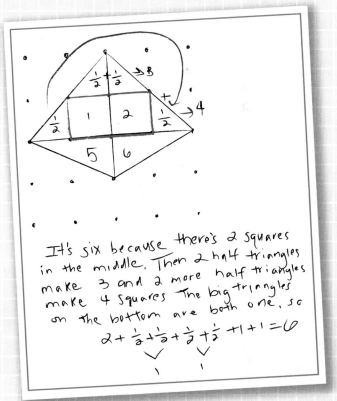

Lucy's Work

Steve's work clearly shows how he combined triangles to make whole squares. He uses arrows to show how he visualized moving triangles around to reconfigure the shape. Although his written explanation does not include all of that information, it is clear from Steve's drawing that he understands how to decompose a shape in order to find its area.

Andrew apparently saw that this figure had at least one line of symmetry, and used this idea in his reasoning. He only counts the area of half of the figure, and then doubles that. He also indicates that he "just knows" that the area of the small triangle is half a square, and that the larger triangle is a whole square.

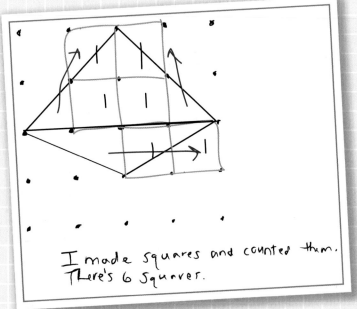

Steve's Work

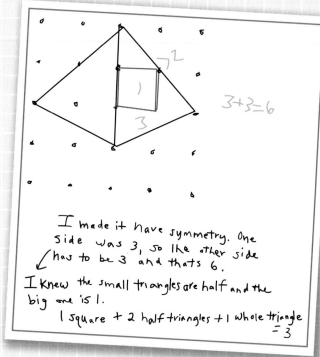

Andrew's Work

Partially Meeting the Benchmark

Students who have correctly decomposed and reconfigured the shape to determine the area, but then either miscounted or left out part of the shape, partially meet the benchmark. Determine whether these are simply errors, or whether there is some aspect of this area work that the student is still unclear about. For example, Noemi correctly made squares and rectangles by moving triangles around the figure. However, she counted the two square-rectangles that resulted from combining the two larger right triangles into one square, which she labeled "5" in her count. From her writing, it seems that she does know that the longer right triangle is equivalent to one square. Students like Noemi should be questioned and asked to go back and doublecheck their work.

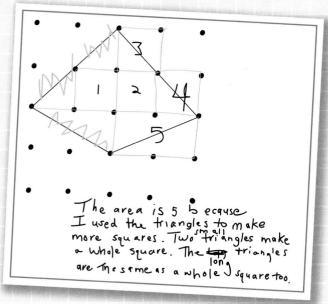

The area is 5 because I used the triangles to make more squares. Two small triangles make a whole square. The long triangles are the same as a whole square too.

Noemi's Work

Not Meeting the Benchmark

Students do not meet the benchmark if they are either unable to decompose and reconfigure the shape in some reasonable way that results in squares that can be counted, or if they are unclear about some basic understanding about measuring area with square units, such as covering the figure completely. Students also do not meet the benchmark if they do not yet understand the relationship between the area of triangles in relation to squares and rectangles, as this is an essential element in finding area with square units. This seems to be the case with Yuki, who labeled every triangle he found in the figure as one half.

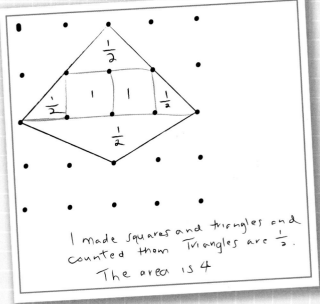

I made squares and triangles and counted them. Triangles are $\frac{1}{2}$. The area is 4

Yuki's Work

Students like Yuki should spend more time working with the area of triangles on the Geoboard. They may use graph paper or dot paper to draw the figures they create, and cut them apart to see how the triangles combine to make rectangles of various sizes. Students who need to work on more general ideas about area, such as completely covering shapes with square units, may benefit from finding the area of given figures with square color tiles.

Describing Polygons

These students are describing attributes that make a figure a polygon. The teacher is recording some of their ideas on a list.

Derek: It can't be a circle or have curved lines.

Teacher writes: It can't have curved lines.

Damian: It has to have corners or points.

Teacher writes: It has corners (*vertices*).

LaTanya: Do they have to have four or more sides?

Teacher: Based on the polygons we've seen, is that a reasonable attribute?

Luke: Is a triangle a polygon?

Andreas: Yes, we should make it less. Two or more sides.

Yuson: I never heard of a shape that has two sides.

Andreas: OK, three or more sides.

Teacher writes: It has three or more sides.

Teacher: What other properties does a polygon have to have?

Yuki: They have to have a line all the way around.

Teacher: [*Tracing the outline of one of the polygons*] This is called a closed shape. What do you think that means?

Ramona: There's no open place at the edge. It's like a dog inside a fenced yard.

Teacher writes: It has a closed shape.

Venetta: Another thing is it doesn't cross over. The lines can't meet in the middle.

Marisol: I know what you mean. It can't be an 8 shape. It has only one space in it.

Teacher: We call it a simple shape. It is just one space.

Richard: Cut them in half and they're even. Like it has to be the same after you fold it. If you fold it in half and if it's still the same shape, then it's a polygon.

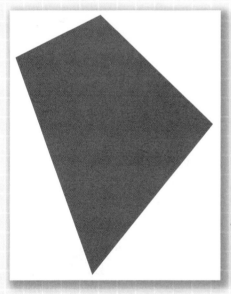

Teacher: What about this shape? What do others think? Does a polygon need to fold in half exactly?

Amelia: No, it can be weird and still be a polygon.

The class ends up with the following list:

Polygons

Must be true:

- It has only straight sides.
- It has three or more sides.
- It has corners (vertices).
- Lengths of sides don't have to be equal.
- It is a closed shape.
- It doesn't have to be a typical shape (like a square or rectangle) or a symmetrical shape that can be folded in half exactly.

Cannot be true:

- It doesn't cross over.
- It can't have curved lines or be a circle.
- It can't have more than one space in it.

By examining a variety of polygons and discussing their observations, students have come up with a list of attributes that define polygons in a fairly comprehensive way. They will refer to this list as they continue to work on describing and identifying polygons throughout this investigation.

Are Squares Rectangles?

This class is discussing quadrilaterals when puzzling questions arise: Is a square a rectangle? Is a rectangle a square? The teacher chooses one shape, a square, on which to center the discussion.

Teacher: What is this [*holding up a square*]: a square, a rectangle, or both?

LaTanya: It's a square.

Jake: But a square is a rectangle, isn't it?

Amelia: No, a rectangle is a square, but a square isn't a rectangle.

Teacher: What do you know has to be true about a square?

Amelia: All 90-degree angles and the sides have to be the same.

Teacher: Okay, for a square, the sides all have to be equal. Now, could we call a square a rectangle?

Helena: A rectangle doesn't have all sides equal; it only has two.

Yuki: A rectangle has two equal sides. It has to have two equal sides, and a square has four equal sides. But in those four equal sides, a square has the two it needs to be a rectangle.

Jill: You know what you could call it? An equilateral rectangle.

Teacher: Jill, can you explain your reasoning? I see some people don't agree.

Jill: A rectangle is four sides that have parallel sides somewhere in the shape. A square has those things, but instead of two sides being different, they're all the same.

Teacher: Amelia, what do you think about that? Can a square be a rectangle, maybe a special kind of rectangle?

Amelia: Well, then you should be able to reverse that too.

Damian: But a rectangle can't always be a square because sometimes two opposite sides are different from the other two sides, and a square *has* to have four equal sides. So I think a square can be a rectangle.

Amelia: I agree, but a rectangle can be a square because it's just the opposite.

Luke: A square can always be a rectangle, but only a rectangle with four equal sides can be a square.

Amelia: But then you'd just call it a square.

Damian: You could call it a square or a rectangle.

Cheyenne: It's like first and last names in families. You can call them square rectangles.

Jake: Or an equilateral rectangle, like Jill said.

Although a number of students made what sounded to them like convincing arguments in this discussion, it is clear to the teacher that not everyone agrees. As the class continues to discuss the properties of quadrilaterals and other polygons, the teacher will help students focus on the relevant attributes of side length and size of angle so that students' classification of polygons becomes more precise.

Building Angles

Students are working on the Math Workshop activity, Building Angles. The teacher visits with several pairs of students as they are working and asks them to tell him about the angles that they have found.

Andrew has placed the acute angles of two Os (*brown rhombuses*) together. He and his partner Lucy both trace the 60-degree angle onto their student sheets.

Teacher: You did that so quickly. How did you know that putting two Os together would make 60 degrees?

Andrew: I knew because one O equals a 30-degree angle.

Teacher: But how did you know that the O shape was 30 degrees?

Lucy: We remembered it from yesterday. We used three Os to build 90 degrees, and 30 and 30 is 60.

Teacher: Is there another way you could make a 60-degree angle?

Andrew: I wonder if there's a shape that has a 15-degree angle.

Teacher: How could that help you?

Andrew: Because then you could put it with the F (*brown right triangle*) which is 45.

Teacher: Do you think you could use one shape to help you find a 15-degree angle?

Lucy: You could use half of the L (*orange right triangle*) to see if it's 15 degrees because this small angle here is 30 degrees too.

Lucy and Andrew are using numerical reasoning as well as what they already know about some of the Power Polygon angles to help them with this task. The teacher moves on to talk with Marisol and Ramona.

Teacher: How did you find out that two Gs (*green rhombus*) would give you 120 degrees?

Marisol: We were experimenting with two Gs and I know that one G is 60 degrees, and 60 plus 60 equals 120.

Teacher: How did you figure out that this angle on G was 60 degrees? Did you just eyeball it, or did you remember from when you made right angles?

Ramona: I knew that J (*yellow isosceles triangle*) is 30, and two Js make a G, and that is how you get 60.

Next the teacher visits Richard and Steve. Richard has put four Os together to form one of his angles.

Richard: I just used four Os and put them like an arrowhead. They're all 30 degrees, and if you count by 30s you get 120, because it takes four 30s to make 120.

Steve: And then you can put another one on—that's 30 more so it's 150.

Richard: Or you can just use a square for 90 degrees, and then you only need two more Os.

Students are using what they know about the measure of some angles to find the measure of other angles. The teacher emphasizes this by asking them to justify the sizes of the angles they are using. These students are becoming flexible in using a variety of shapes to measure the angles they need to build. They are noticing that they can find 30- and 60-degree angles in both triangles and quadrilaterals, and using these in different combinations to make larger angles. The teacher knows that through this work, students are building an understanding of the relative size of angles—that 15 degrees is relatively small, that 45 degrees is half of 90 degrees, and that obtuse angles are larger than 90 degrees.

Dividing Crazy Cakes

Students are dividing Crazy Cakes on *Student Activity Book* pages 58–59. After the initial discussion, the teacher begins circulating around the room, observing and questioning students as they divide the crazy cakes. She finds that students are challenged by finding the area of these irregular polygons, but she also notices that the activity is building a stronger understanding of area.

The teacher stops and watches Ursula divide Crazy Cake #2. She notices Ursula has decomposed the figure (made smaller parts) and then used congruence to show how the pieces are equal.

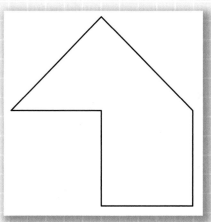

Ursula: When I looked at the shape, I realized that if I cut the triangle in the top in half, and the square in half, I'd have four triangles the same size. So each person would get the same amount.

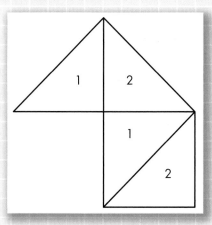

Next, the teacher watches Yuson and Derek. She notices that both of these students are decomposing and reconfiguring the shapes to create a new shape that is symmetrical. She asks them to explain how they divided the crazy cakes.

Yuson: I just cut the triangle in half, and then I looked at it awhile. I flipped and turned the triangle on the left, so then I had a rectangle. That was easy to cut in half so each person gets the same amount.

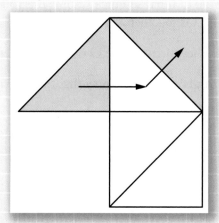

Derek: This one was easy. First I drew a line separating the triangle and the square. Then I cut the square in half, and moved the one triangle, so then I had a diamond, and cut it in half. The symmetry shows both sides are equal.

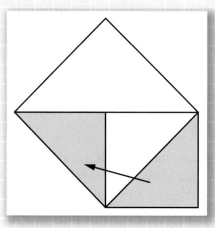

Teacher: Interesting. Is that shape a diamond?

Derek: Oh, I guess it's a square!

Teacher: How do you know it has the same area? You both changed the shape of the cake.

Yuson: But it's not like I threw part of the cake away or fed it to the dog or anything. I just cut a piece and put it somewhere else.

Derek: Right—it's the same amount of cake, it's just put together differently. And I'm convinced they're the same—I wouldn't care which half of the crazy cake I got—they're both the same.

The teacher moves on and watches Emaan work on Crazy Cake #5. Emaan uses the same strategy that Yuson and Derek used—reconfiguring the shape to make one that is symmetrical.

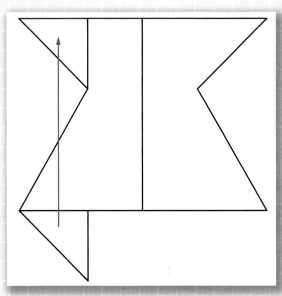

Venetta is using the same strategy as Ursula—she decomposes the figure and uses congruence to show how the pieces are equal. The teacher asks Venetta to explain what she did.

Venetta: I saw a rectangle inside the shape, so first I drew in lines to make that. Then I drew a line down the middle of it—so each person would get the same amount. I looked at the shape some more, and drew a line to make a triangle out of the little piece at the bottom of the shape. Then I saw there were two bigger triangles on each side that were the same size, and two little triangles that were the same size. So each person would get a rectangle, a big triangle, and a little triangle. It's the same area.

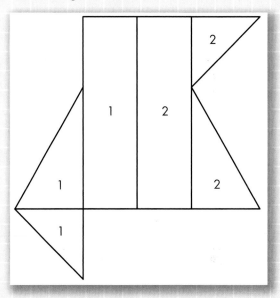

As the teacher is circulating, she is watching for strategies she knows students typically use. She notices Ursula and Venetta decomposing the shape into smaller pieces, and then matching congruent pieces so each person would get the same amount. She sees Yuson, Derek, and Emaan moving pieces of the shape in some way to create a shape with line symmetry so it is easy to see each area is $\frac{1}{2}$. She questions Derek and Yuson to see whether they realize the new shapes they created have the same area as the original shape. The teacher realizes that as students work on breaking apart a shape and rearranging it into a different shape with the same area, they are developing strategies that will support the development of formulas for the area of various polygons. The teacher plans on highlighting this idea in the whole class discussions about Crazy Cake #6.

Student Math Handbook

The *Student Math Handbook* pages related to this unit are pictured on the following pages. This book is designed to be used flexibly: as a resource for students doing classwork, as a book students can take home for reference while doing homework and playing math games with their families, and as a reference for families to better understand the work their children are doing in class.

When students take the *Student Math Handbook* home, they and their families can discuss these pages together to reinforce or enhance students' understanding of the mathematical concepts and games in this unit.

Fractions of an Area

Enrique, Helena, Amelia, and Luke have one sandwich to share equally. How much of the sandwich will each of them get?

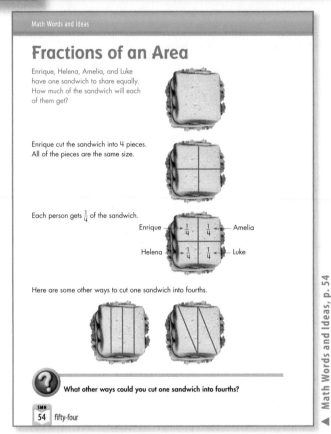

Enrique cut the sandwich into 4 pieces. All of the pieces are the same size.

Each person gets $\frac{1}{4}$ of the sandwich.

Enrique — $\frac{1}{4}$ | $\frac{1}{4}$ — Amelia
Helena — $\frac{1}{4}$ | $\frac{1}{4}$ — Luke

Here are some other ways to cut one sandwich into fourths.

? What other ways could you cut one sandwich into fourths?

SMH 54 fifty-four

◀ Math Words and Ideas, p. 54

Linear Measurement (page 1 of 2)

By measuring length you can answer questions such as the following:

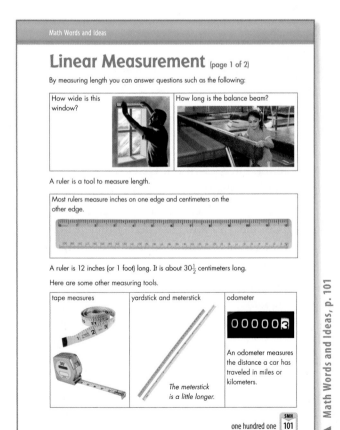

How wide is this window?

How long is the balance beam?

A ruler is a tool to measure length.

Most rulers measure inches on one edge and centimeters on the other edge.

A ruler is 12 inches (or 1 foot) long. It is about $30\frac{1}{2}$ centimeters long.

Here are some other measuring tools.

tape measures	yardstick and meterstick	odometer
		000003
	The meterstick is a little longer.	An odometer measures the distance a car has traveled in miles or kilometers.

one hundred one **SMH 101**

◀ Math Words and Ideas, p. 101

Linear Measurement (page 2 of 2)

There are two different systems of measuring length.

People in the United States use the U.S. standard system to measure most lengths, using inches, feet, yards, and miles. Only two other countries in the world—Liberia and Myanmar—use this measurement system.

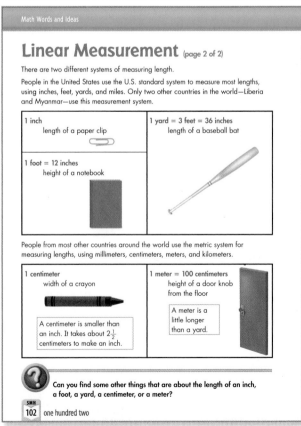

1 inch
   length of a paper clip

1 yard = 3 feet = 36 inches
   length of a baseball bat

1 foot = 12 inches
   height of a notebook

People from most other countries around the world use the metric system for measuring lengths, using millimeters, centimeters, meters, and kilometers.

1 centimeter
   width of a crayon

A centimeter is smaller than an inch. It takes about $2\frac{1}{2}$ centimeters to make an inch.

1 meter = 100 centimeters
   height of a door knob
   from the floor

A meter is a little longer than a yard.

? Can you find some other things that are about the length of an inch, a foot, a yard, a centimeter, or a meter?

SMH 102 one hundred two

◀ Math Words and Ideas, p. 102

Measuring Accurately

The students in Ms. Smith's class used rulers to measure the length of the chalkboard tray in their classroom. Even though the students measured the same distance, they got several different answers.

Look at the pictures below and look for the measurement mistakes the students made.

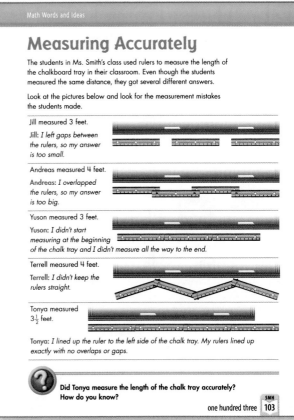

Jill measured 3 feet.

Jill: I left gaps between the rulers, so my answer is too small.

Andreas measured 4 feet.

Andreas: I overlapped the rulers, so my answer is too big.

Yuson measured 3 feet.

Yuson: I didn't start measuring at the beginning of the chalk tray and I didn't measure all the way to the end.

Terrell measured 4 feet.

Terrell: I didn't keep the rulers straight.

Tonya measured $3\frac{1}{2}$ feet.

Tonya: I lined up the ruler to the left side of the chalk tray. My rulers lined up exactly with no overlaps or gaps.

Did Tonya measure the length of the chalk tray accurately? How do you know?

Perimeter (page 1 of 2)

Math Words
• perimeter

Perimeter is the length of the border of a figure. Perimeter is a linear measure.

An ant walks around the perimeter of the top of a desk by starting at one corner, walking all the way around the border, and ending at the same corner where it started.

How far did the ant walk?

What is the perimeter of the top of this desk?

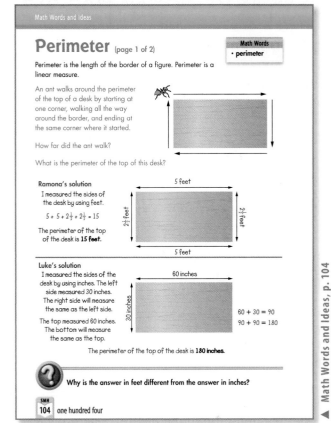

Ramona's solution

I measured the sides of the desk by using feet.

$5 + 5 + 2\frac{1}{2} + 2\frac{1}{2} = 15$

The perimeter of the top of the desk is **15 feet.**

5 feet
$2\frac{1}{2}$ feet
$2\frac{1}{2}$ feet
5 feet

Luke's solution

I measured the sides of the desk by using inches. The left side measured 30 inches. The right side will measure the same as the left side.

The top measured 60 inches. The bottom will measure the same as the top.

60 inches
30 inches

$60 + 30 = 90$
$90 + 90 = 180$

The perimeter of the top of the desk is **180 inches.**

Why is the answer in feet different from the answer in inches?

Perimeter (page 2 of 2)

Fill in the missing measures and find the perimeter.

Use the *LogoPaths* software to solve problems about perimeter.

Helena's solution

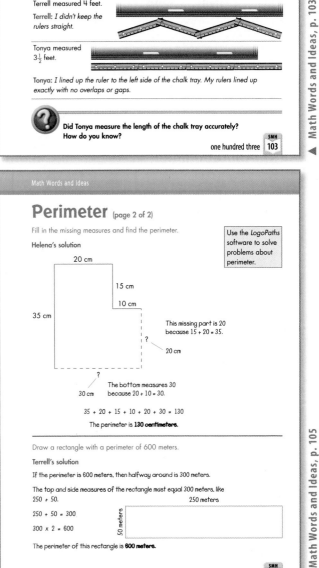

20 cm
15 cm
10 cm
35 cm
This missing part is 20 because 15 + 20 = 35.
20 cm
?
?
30 cm
The bottom measures 30 because 20 + 10 = 30.

$35 + 20 + 15 + 10 + 20 + 30 = 130$

The perimeter is 130 centimeters.

Draw a rectangle with a perimeter of 600 meters.

Terrell's solution

If the perimeter is 600 meters, then halfway around is 300 meters.

The top and side measures of the rectangle must equal 300 meters, like 250 + 50.

$250 + 50 = 300$

$300 \times 2 = 600$

250 meters
50 meters

The perimeter of this rectangle is 600 meters.

Polygons

Math Words
• polygon
• two-dimensional (2-D)

Polygons are closed two-dimensional (2-D) figures with straight sides.

These figures are polygons.

These figures are not polygons.

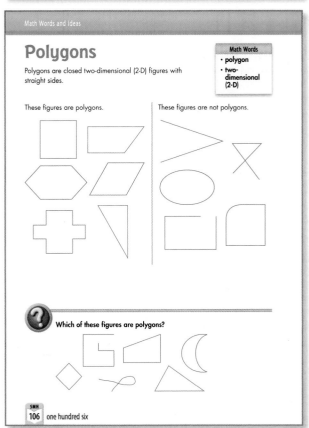

Which of these figures are polygons?

Naming Polygons

Polygons are named for the number of sides they have.

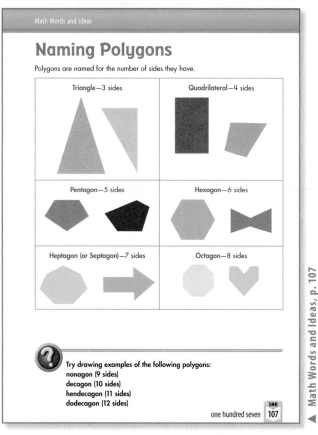

Triangle—3 sides

Quadrilateral—4 sides

Pentagon—5 sides

Hexagon—6 sides

Heptagon (or Septagon)—7 sides

Octagon—8 sides

? Try drawing examples of the following polygons:
nonagon (9 sides)
decagon (10 sides)
hendecagon (11 sides)
dodecagon (12 sides)

one hundred seven **SMH 107**

▲ Math Words and Ideas, p. 107

Quadrilaterals (page 1 of 2)

Math Words
• quadrilateral
• rhombus

A quadrilateral is a polygon that has all of the following features:

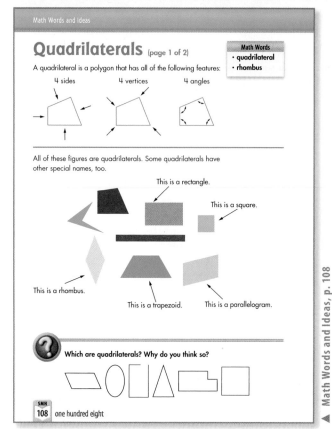

4 sides

4 vertices

4 angles

All of these figures are quadrilaterals. Some quadrilaterals have other special names, too.

This is a rectangle.

This is a square.

This is a rhombus.

This is a trapezoid.

This is a parallelogram.

? Which are quadrilaterals? Why do you think so?

SMH 108 one hundred eight

▲ Math Words and Ideas, p. 108

Quadrilaterals (page 2 of 2)

Math Words
• parallel
• trapezoid
• parallelogram

Parallel lines go in the same direction and are equidistant from each other, as railroad tracks do.

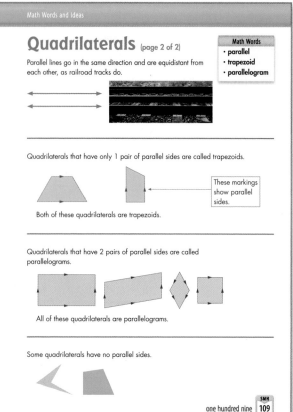

Quadrilaterals that have only 1 pair of parallel sides are called trapezoids.

These markings show parallel sides.

Both of these quadrilaterals are trapezoids.

Quadrilaterals that have 2 pairs of parallel sides are called parallelograms.

All of these quadrilaterals are parallelograms.

Some quadrilaterals have no parallel sides.

one hundred nine **SMH 109**

▲ Math Words and Ideas, p. 109

Rectangles and Squares

Math Words
• rectangle
• square

A rectangle is a special kind of quadrilateral that has the following features:

• 4 sides
• 4 vertices
• 4 angles that all measure 90° (right angles)

You can read more about right angles on page 111.

Here are some rectangles.

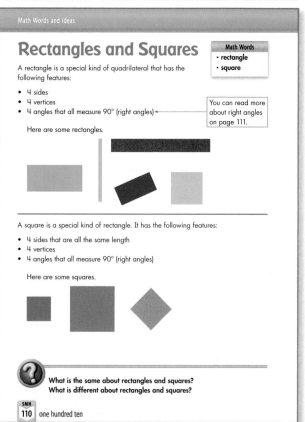

A square is a special kind of rectangle. It has the following features:

• 4 sides that are all the same length
• 4 vertices
• 4 angles that all measure 90° (right angles)

Here are some squares.

? What is the same about rectangles and squares?
What is different about rectangles and squares?

SMH 110 one hundred ten

▲ Math Words and Ideas, p. 110

Angles (page 1 of 3)

Math Words
• angle
• degrees
• right angle

The measure of an angle in a polygon is the amount of turn between two sides.

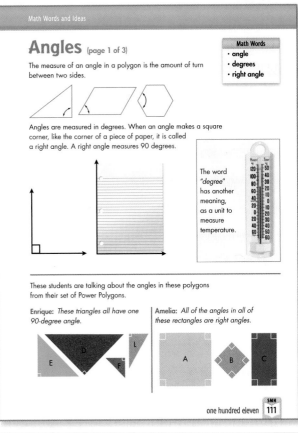

Angles are measured in degrees. When an angle makes a square corner, like the corner of a piece of paper, it is called a right angle. A right angle measures 90 degrees.

The word "*degree*" has another meaning, as a unit to measure temperature.

These students are talking about the angles in these polygons from their set of Power Polygons.

Enrique: These triangles all have one 90-degree angle.

Amelia: All of the angles in all of these rectangles are right angles.

one hundred eleven **SMH 111**

◀ **Math Words and Ideas, p. 111**

Angles (page 2 of 3)

Math Words
• acute angle
• obtuse angle

Helena: *None of the angles in this trapezoid measures 90 degrees.*

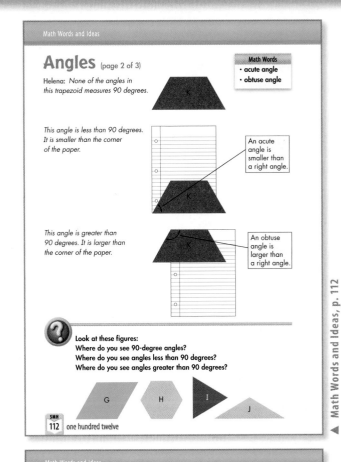

This angle is less than 90 degrees. It is smaller than the corner of the paper.

An acute angle is smaller than a right angle.

This angle is greater than 90 degrees. It is larger than the corner of the paper.

An obtuse angle is larger than a right angle.

Look at these figures:
Where do you see 90-degree angles?
Where do you see angles less than 90 degrees?
Where do you see angles greater than 90 degrees?

SMH 112 one hundred twelve

◀ **Math Words and Ideas, p. 112**

Angles (page 3 of 3)

How many degrees are in this angle?

How do you know?

Amelia's solution
I can use two of these triangles to make a square.

$$45 + 45 = 90$$

These two angles together make 90°, and they are equal, so each angle measures 45°.

How many degrees are in this angle?

How do you know?

Enrique's solution
When I put three of the hexagons together, three of the angles make a circle in the middle.

$$360 \div 3 = 120$$

The circle has 360°, so each angle is 120°.

You can use the *LogoPaths* software to solve problems about angles.

How many degrees are in this angle?
How do you know?

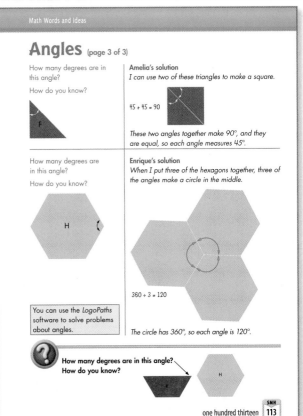

one hundred thirteen **SMH 113**

◀ **Math Words and Ideas, p. 113**

Area

Math Words
• area
• square foot

Area is the amount of surface a figure covers. Area is a measure of 2-D space.

Richard and his uncle plan to build a tiled patio. They will use square tiles, 1 foot on a side. Here is a sketch of their patio design.

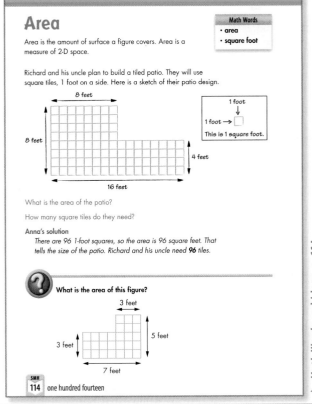

1 foot →
1 foot ↓
This is 1 square foot.

What is the area of the patio?

How many square tiles do they need?

Anna's solution
*There are 96 1-foot squares, so the area is 96 square feet. That tells the size of the patio. Richard and his uncle need **96** tiles.*

What is the area of this figure?

3 feet
5 feet
3 feet
7 feet

SMH 114 one hundred fourteen

◀ **Math Words and Ideas, p. 114**

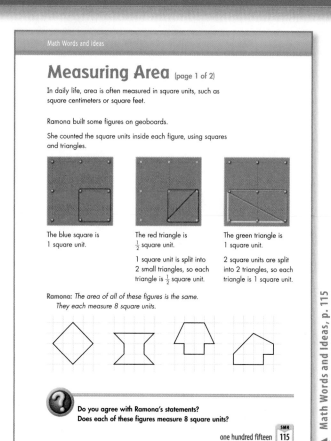

Measuring Area (page 1 of 2)

In daily life, area is often measured in square units, such as square centimeters or square feet.

Ramona built some figures on geoboards.

She counted the square units inside each figure, using squares and triangles.

The blue square is 1 square unit.

The red triangle is $\frac{1}{2}$ square unit.

1 square unit is split into 2 small triangles, so each triangle is $\frac{1}{2}$ square unit.

The green triangle is 1 square unit.

2 square units are split into 2 triangles, so each triangle is 1 square unit.

Ramona: *The area of all of these figures is the same. They each measure 8 square units.*

? Do you agree with Ramona's statements? Does each of these figures measure 8 square units?

one hundred fifteen **115**

▲ Math Words and Ideas, p. 115

Measuring Area (page 2 of 2)

While area is often measured in square units, it can also be measured with other shapes.

Anna used Power Polygons to build a figure.

She measured the area of her figure using triangle N.

The area of my design is 14 triangle Ns.

116 one hundred sixteen

▲ Math Words and Ideas, p. 116

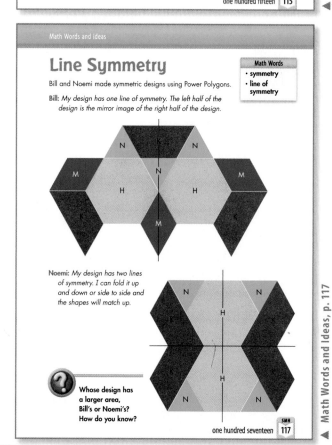

Line Symmetry

Math Words
• symmetry
• line of symmetry

Bill and Noemi made symmetric designs using Power Polygons.

Bill: *My design has one line of symmetry. The left half of the design is the mirror image of the right half of the design.*

Noemi: *My design has two lines of symmetry. I can fold it up and down or side to side and the shapes will match up.*

? Whose design has a larger area, Bill's or Noemi's? How do you know?

one hundred seventeen **117**

▲ Math Words and Ideas, p. 117

Index

IN THIS UNIT